$ 19.95.  11/23/99  Chelsea

T

# CUBA

# MAJOR WORLD NATIONS
# CUBA

Clifford W. Crouch

CHELSEA HOUSE PUBLISHERS
Philadelphia

**Chelsea House Publishers**

*Contributing Author:* Miriam Seidel

Copyright © 1999 by Chelsea House Publishers,
a division of Main Line Book Co.
All rights reserved.
Printed and bound in the United States of America.

**Library of Congress Cataloging-in-Publication Data**

Crouch, Clifford W.
Cuba / Clifford W. Crouch.
p.   cm. — (Major world nations)
Includes index.
Summary: A social, cultural, political, and economic study
of Cuba and its people.
ISBN 0–7910–4736–9
1. Cuba—Juvenile literature.   [1. Cuba.]
I. Title.   II. Series.
F1758.5.C76   1997
972.91—dc21   97–23543
CIP
AC

# CONTENTS

Map                                             6

Facts at a Glance                               9

History at a Glance                             11

Chapter 1  Cuba and the World                   15

Chapter 2  The Pearl of the Antilles            19

Chapter 3  Settlement and Slavery               29

Chapter 4  Rebellion                            39

*Color Section*  Scenes of Cuba                 49

Chapter 5  Cuba Under Castro                     69

Chapter 6  The Cuban Way of Life                77

Chapter 7  The Party and Government             87

Chapter 8  The Arts                             95

Chapter 9  The Future of Cuba                   105

Glossary                                        107

Index                                           110

GULF OF MEXICO

Matanzas

Havana

SIERRA DE
LOS ÓRGANOS

PINAR
DEL RÍO

HAVANA

Bellam
Cave

Viñales

Pinar
del Río

SIERRA
DEL
ROSARIO

MATANZA

Peninsula de
Guanahacabibes

BAY OF PI
(PLAYA GIRÓ

ISLE OF YOUTH

UNITED STATES

ATLANTIC OCEAN

GULF OF MEXICO

Bahamas

Yucatán

Cuba

Dominican
Republic

MEXICO

Jamaica

Haiti

Puerto Rico

LESSER
ANTILLES

GREATER ANTILLES

Central America

CARIBBEAN SEA

Panama

South America

ATLANTIC OCEAN

VILLA
CLARA

NFUEGOS     • Santa
             Clara

• Cienfuegos

IERRA
DEL
CAMBRAY     SANCTI SPÍRITUS     Caonao
                               River

         • Sancti    CIEGO
           Spíritus  DE AVILA

Trinidad

                     • Camagüey

         CAMAGÜEY                          Holguín

                            LAS TUNAS     HOLGUÍN

                     Cauto River
                                  SANTIAGO              Baracoa
                                  DE CUBA   GUANTÁNAMO •
              GRANMA             • Cobre
                                           • Guantánamo

SIERRA MAESTRA        PICO      Santiago
                      TURQUINO  de Cuba    GUANTÁNAMO BAY

CARIBBEAN SEA

# FACTS AT A GLANCE

## Land and People

| | |
|---|---|
| **Area** | 44,218 square miles (114,524 square kilometers) |
| **Mountains** | Sierra de los Órganos, Sierra del Rosario, Sierra del Escambray, and Sierra Maestra |
| **Highest Point** | Pico Real del Turquino, 6,500 feet (1,982 meters) |
| **Climate** | 60° to 90° Fahrenheit (16° to 32° centigrade) |
| **Population** | 11.1 million (1996) |
| **Population Density** | 256 people per square mile (99 per square kilometer) |
| **Population Distribution** | Urban, 74 percent; rural, 26 percent |
| **Capital** | Havana (population 2.2 million) |
| **Major Cities** | Santiago de Cuba (444,000), Camagüey, (294,000), Holguín (242,000) |
| **Official Language** | Spanish |
| **Religions** | Christianity (primarily Roman Catholic), Santería and other Afro-Cuban religions; freedom of worship restricted |
| **Ethnic Groups** | Spanish, mulatto, black, and Chinese |
| **Literacy Rate** | 96 percent (1996) |

9

| | |
|---|---|
| **Average Life Expectancy** | Male, 73 years; female, 77 years |
| **Infant Mortality Rate** | 8 per 1,000 live births |

# Economy

| | |
|---|---|
| **Mineral Resources** | Nickel, cobalt, copper, chromium |
| **Major Cash Crops** | Sugar, tobacco, citrus fruits, coffee |
| **Industries** | Food processing, tourism, textiles, cigarettes |
| **Currency** | Peso divided into 100 centavos |
| **Major Exports** | Sugar, nickel, fruit, fish, tobacco, and coffee |
| **Major Imports** | Machinery, oil, food, pharmaceuticals, and steel |
| **Major Trading Partners** | Canada, China, Russia, Spain, and Mexico |

# Government

| | |
|---|---|
| **Form of Government** | Communist state, headed by the leader of the Communist party of Cuba |
| **Constitution** | Approved by plebiscite in 1976, revised 1992 |
| **Government Bodies** | Executive, including a council of ministers; legislative (indirect election); judicial (accountable to other branches) |
| **National Administrative Divisions** | 14 provinces, 169 municipalities |
| **Head of State** | President and first secretary of the Communist party |
| **Other Chief Officials** | First vice-president and minister of the Revolutionary Armed Forces |
| **Political Party** | Communist Party of Cuba (Partido Comunista de Cuba, or PCC) |
| **Eligibility to Vote** | Universal over 16 except for those who have applied to emigrate |

# HISTORY AT A GLANCE

| | |
|---|---|
| **pre-Columbian Era** | Island is inhabited by Indian tribes, including the Taíno, arriving from Central and South America. |
| **1492** | The explorer Christopher Columbus lands and claims the island for Spain. |
| **1511** | Spanish settlement, led by Diego Velásquez, begins with Baracoa, the first permanent city. |
| **late 1500s** | Indian population dies out through war, ill treatment, and disease. |
| **1600s** | The era of Caribbean piracy by English, French, and Dutch buccaneers begins. |
| **1655** | The British seize the neighboring island of Jamaica. |
| **1713** | The Treaty of Utrecht allows England to engage in slave trade with the Spanish colonies, including Cuba. |
| **1762–63** | The British capture and then relinquish Havana. |
| **1791–1804** | A slave revolt on the island of Hispaniola leads to the founding of Haiti and the relocation of refugees to Cuba; the beginning of Cuba's slave-and-sugar economy. |

| | |
|---|---|
| **1808** | Napoléon occupies Spain. |
| **1810–24** | Spain's South American colonies revolt, leaving Cuba as its major colony. |
| **1868–78** | Ten Years' War for independence ends, and Cuba is defeated; the Pact of Zanjón. |
| **1879** | La Guerra Chiquita (The Little War) fails. |
| **1886** | The practice of slavery ends in Cuba. |
| **1895** | War of Independence begins; revolutionary leader José Martí is killed in battle. |
| **1898** | After the USS *Maine* explodes, the United States declares war on Spain and wins. |
| **1899–1901** | United States maintains provisional military government in Cuba. |
| **1902** | The Republic of Cuba is formed and Tomás Estrada Palma is elected president. |
| **1906–09** | The second U.S. provisional government is established as a result of armed clashes between Cuban political parties. |
| **1925–33** | Gerardo Machado becomes Cuba's first military dictator. |
| **1940–44** | Fulgencio Batista serves as president. |
| **1934** | Platt Amendment, which permitted U.S. intervention in Cuba since 1902, is terminated. |
| **1940** | A new constitution is enacted. |
| **1952** | Batista assumes complete power in a military revolt. |
| **1953** | On July 26, Fidel Castro and his followers attack Moncada barracks in Santiago de Cuba, but the plan to overthrow Batista fails. |
| **1959** | Castro, assisted by his brother Raúl and Ernesto "Che" Guevara, takes control of the country after three years of guerrilla warfare. |

**1960** Cuba and the Soviet Union establish close diplomatic and economic ties.

**1961** Cuban exile forces, supported by the United States, land at the Bay of Pigs and fail in their attempt to overthrow Castro.

**1962** The United States and the Soviet Union come to the brink of nuclear war after the Soviets install nuclear missiles in Cuba; Soviets finally agree to their withdrawal.

**1975** Soviet-armed Cuban troops are sent to Angola to counter South Africa's attack on the new Communist government.

**1976** A new constitution based on a Soviet model is enacted.

**1980** An estimated 125,000 Cubans flee Cuba from the port of Mariel after Castro temporarily allows emigration.

**1983** U.S. forces oust almost 1,000 Cuban troops from the island of Grenada.

**1990** Special Period in Peacetime tightens food rations following cutbacks in aid from the Soviet Union.

**1991** The dissolution of the Soviet Union, Cuba's greatest source of aid and primary trading partner, plunges Cuba into deep economic crisis.

**1993** Self-employment in many trades is legalized, and Cubans are allowed to hold U.S. currency.

**1994** 35,000 Cubans emigrate to U.S. in small rafts.

**1996** After four Cuban-Americans are shot down by Cuban pilots, U.S. passes Helms-Burton Act, allowing suits in U.S. courts against investors in properties lost during the Revolution.

*A beach on the Isle of Youth, which lies to the south of Cuba proper, is a popular recreational spot. Until the 18th century, the isle was a haven for pirates; later the British writer Robert Louis Stevenson used it for the setting of his adventure novel* Treasure Island, *presumably because many treasure-laden ships were sunk off the island's coast.*

# 1

# Cuba and the World

The island of Cuba, an independent nation, is the largest island of the West Indies. It was discovered in 1492 by Christopher Columbus, who was sailing under the Spanish flag, and remained under Spain's rule for almost four centuries. Over the centuries, the island has endured hurricanes, diseases, pirates, wars between rival European powers, its own fight for independence, corrupt government by its own leaders, and intrusions by both the United States and the Soviet Union.

Cuba was one of the last nations in the Western Hemisphere to abolish slavery, and today the island's culture continues to be a remarkable, vital blend of Spanish and African traditions. In both the visual arts and music—especially in what is called Afro-Cuban jazz—the island has an international reputation. Yet as the 20th century draws to a close, Cuba is probably best known as the home base of Fidel Castro, one of the most controversial political leaders in the world.

Castro has ruled Cuba since 1959, and his critics call him an aging dictator who has imprisoned, executed, or exiled all of his opponents. Critics note that in his four decades of power Castro

*An overseer supervises the harvesting of sugarcane in the early 1900s. Today, Cuba is the world's greatest exporter of sugar.*

has never subjected himself to a popular election, and they suggest that his real source of power was the Soviet Union, which until 1990 subsidized the country with at least $5 billion in economic aid each year.

Castro's defenders, in turn, point to significant improvements in the nation's literacy rate and its health care. Education is free in Cuba, new schools have been constructed in many rural areas, and the literacy rate rose from 75 percent in 1955 to 96 percent in 1996. The government-run health care system, which includes many rural clinics, is widely considered one of the best in the Third World.

Both Castro's opponents and admirers, however, concede that he has made Cuba one of the most prominent countries in the world for its relatively small size and population. Its military force is the second largest in South America and has engaged in combat around the globe. Castro, whose beard and battle fatigues have become trademarks, is one of the most widely recognized figures alive.

Domestically, Cuba continues to be troubled by a number of severe problems. The fall of the Soviet Union in 1991 plunged Cuba into the worst economic crisis in its history, causing great hardships among the already poor populace. In the face of the continuing economic embargo by the United States, Cuba has forged new economic alliances with other countries, notably Canada, Spain, and Mexico, with major initiatives in tourism and mining helping to rebuild its economy.

Some limited social change has also been allowed: self-employment in many trades has been legalized, along with farmers' markets; and Cubans may now hold U.S. currency. But while Castro still leads, substantive electoral reform and the expansion of social freedoms seem unlikely. The future of Cuba, by the mid-1990s one of the few countries in the world still led by a Communist regime, holds compelling questions for itself and the world.

*An early engraving of one of Cuba's tropical rain forests depicts some of the grandeur of nature that Columbus might have seen when he discovered the island in October 1492.*

# 2

# The Pearl of the Antilles

In October 1492, Italian explorer Christopher Columbus wrote about the island of Cuba:

> This island is the most beautiful that eyes have seen, full of good harbors and deep rivers . . . full of very beautiful mountains, although they are not very extensive as regards length, but high. . . . The songs of the birds and the chirping of crickets throughout the night lulled everyone to rest, while the air was soft and healthy, and the nights neither hot nor cold.

Columbus had been employed by King Ferdinand V and Queen Isabella of Spain to discover a new route to India and the opulent Spice Islands of Southeast Asia. But the explorer had not found this route; in fact, he discovered a part of the world previously unknown to Europe, the islands of the West Indies. The vast expanses to the north and south, beyond Columbus's view, were the continents of the Americas, the lands that became known as the New World. (Because he thought he had arrived in the Indies, he called the native people he met there Indians.)

*The slopes of the Sierra de los Órganos descend into the Viñales Valley of the province of Pinar del Río, an area noted for its rich tobacco land. The cliffs of this valley contain many picturesque caverns and beautiful underground rivers.*

Cuba is the largest in a chain of islands, called an archipelago, that stretches across the Caribbean Sea. Most of the islands in the West Indies are part of a group called the Antilles. The Antilles, in turn, are divided into two groups: the Lesser Antilles, which consists of the smaller islands to the east, including the Virgin Islands, Martinique, Barbados, and Grenada; and the Greater Antilles, which includes the four large islands to the west—Puerto Rico, Hispaniola, Jamaica, and Cuba. Because of its natural beauty and pleasant climate, Cuba has been popularly nicknamed "the pearl of the Antilles."

The westernmost island of the Greater Antilles, Cuba lies at the entrance to the Gulf of Mexico. It is 90 miles (145 kilometers) south of Key West, Florida, and 130 miles (210 kilometers) east of Mexico's Yucatán peninsula. On a clear day, the island of Jamaica is visible 87 miles (140 kilometers) to the south of Cuba; to the southeast, about 50 miles (80 kilometers) away, are the nations of Haiti and the Dominican Republic on the island of Hispaniola.

## Geographic Features

Long and narrow, Cuba measures slightly more than 750 miles (1,210 kilometers) in length and averages only about 60 miles (97 kilometers) in width. The island is surrounded by thousands of tiny islets, or cays. Of these, the largest is the Isla de la Juventud, or Isle of Youth (formerly called the Isla de Pinos, or Isle of Pines, but renamed because many young Cubans are schooled there)—an island approximately 900 square miles (2,331 square kilometers) lying just off the southern coast. When all these islets are combined with the main island, the area of land Cuba occupies is close to 44,218 square miles (114,524 square kilometers), a region about the size of the U.S. state of Pennsylvania.

Cuba is divided into 14 provinces, from west to east: Pinar del Río, City of Havana, Havana, Matanzas, Villa Clara, Cienfuegos, Sancti Spíritus, Ciego de Avila, Camagüey, Las Tunas, Holguín, Granma, Santiago de Cuba, and Guantánamo. The Isle of Youth is a special municipality.

More than half of the country consists of flat or gently rolling plains. Whereas the northern coastline tends to be rocky and steep, the southern coastline is more often marked by lowland marshes and rain forests. There are more than 130 beaches along Cuba's

*The Yumurí Valley in Matanzas province has gently rolling plains. The Yumurí and San Juan rivers flow through the province, making the soil fertile for growing coffee and tobacco.*

coasts. One of the most popular is Varadero Beach in the north, 10 miles (16 kilometers) of fine white sand that became a playground for the rich and famous during the early 1900s.

Four major mountain ranges rise across the island and increase in height from the west to the east. In the far west stand the Sierra de los Órganos, and slightly to the southeast are the crags of the Sierra del Rosario; both ranges have many beautiful hills and valleys. In the central part of Cuba are the Sierra del Escambray, one of the island's loveliest regions; it is also the site of Lake Hanabanilla, which was artificially created in the early 1960s. The chief range, however, is the Sierra Maestra, which rise steeply from the southeastern coast. These rugged mountains, the country's highest, are capped by the Pico Real del Turquino, which reaches an altitude of about 6,500 feet (1,982 meters).

In addition to its mountain ranges, Cuba has many cliffs and valleys, particularly the Viñales Valley west of Havana and the Yumurí Valley in the north, which contains the massive cave of Bellamar, known for its magnificent crystalline stalagmites and stalagtites as well as underground streams. Cuba has many rivers, but most are short and shallow and are therefore unnavigable. The major waterway is the Río Cauto, or Cautious River, which extends some 230 miles (370 kilometers) throughout the southeast and runs out of the Sierra Maestra and into the Bay of Guacanayabo.

## Climate and Weather

The flow of the Río Cauto, like that of Cuba's other rivers, varies greatly with seasonal rainfall. Because Cuba lies between the geographic lines called the Tropic of Cancer and the Tropic of Capricorn—a region known as the torrid zone—it is considered a tropical country. Each year it experiences two major seasons: one rainy (from May to October) and the other dry (from November to April). During wetter periods, Cuba sometimes has 8 inches (205 millimeters) of rainfall a month.

*Firemen and workers clean up Matanzas, the provincial capital, after a hurricane ripped through the town in 1948. Matanzas is located on a bay on the northern coast of Cuba and is thus susceptible to damage caused by tropical storms and hurricanes.*

The end of the rainy season in the West Indies is often marked by the formation of tropical storms and hurricanes. These vast, ocean-generated cyclones can measure hundreds of miles in diameter and disgorge torrential rains and winds of 80 to 130 miles per hour or more. When a hurricane hits land, the downpour frequently gives rise to ruinous floods, destructive winds, and tornadoes—rotating funnels of air with winds up to 300 miles per hour.

Cuba, like most of the Caribbean and Gulf Coast region, has experienced death and devastation from hurricanes. One storm in October 1926 left more than 600 Cubans dead, and Hurricane Flora, which struck in October 1963, left 6,000 dead in Cuba and Haiti. These, however, were the worst tempests to have hit a country that is otherwise renowned for its mild weather. Because Cuba is near the equator, gentle northeastern winds blow in from the Atlantic Ocean both in winter and in summer. A warm ocean current called the Gulf Stream also helps to keep the temperature along the Cuban shoreline fairly constant. Temperatures across the island range from around 60 °F (16 °C) in January to around 90 °F (32 °C) in August but generally hover within a few degrees of the annual average temperature of 78 °F (25 °C).

## Plant and Animal Life

A variety of tropical plants grow easily under the congenial conditions in Cuba. The sweet-smelling white *mariposa*, or butterfly jasmine, is the national flower and was worn as a symbol of patriotism during Cuba's wars for independence. Among the best-known flowering plants to blossom during the rainy season are the bougainvillea, oleander, frangipani (red jasmine), and buddleia. The water hyacinth, an aquatic flower, grows so profusely that its vines sometimes clog canals and other waterways. On some sandy shores are found some kinds of cacti and the sea grape, which bears clusters of edible blue berries. Many varieties of bamboo flourish on the island, in addition to a thorny shrub called the *huisache*, or aroma bush.

When Columbus first explored Cuba, he noted numerous plants that the native people used in making food, medicine, and clothing. Among these were cotton, gourds, pumpkins, and beans. Two native vegetables that are still widely cultivated today are cassava, or manioc, a plant whose roots resemble the sweet potato and can be eaten in the same way or ground into flour, and maize, also called Indian corn.

The most famous plant that Columbus's crew found in use among the Indian people was tobacco. When the explorers first beheld Indians inhaling smoke from burning rolls of dried tobacco leaves—the predecessors of the now-famous Havana cigar—the spectacle was entirely new to them. Today tobacco is still a major agricultural crop for Cuba.

Some vegetation that today occurs naturally in Cuba was unknown there before the arrival of Europeans. In 1492, Columbus made note of many species of palm trees, such as the royal and thatch palms; the coconut-bearing palm, however, grew in Cuba only after it was imported from the coasts of Southeast Asia. Some other trees from the eastern tropics have also prospered after being transplanted to Cuba—for example, the teak and banyan (from India) and the tulip tree (from Africa).

Among the trees native to the island are mahogany, cedar, and West Indian ebony, which are found in the southern lowlands and rain forests. Some swamps are densely populated with the mangrove tree, recognized by the spaghettilike tangle of its roots, which protrude above ground. Pine and oak predominate in the sandier highlands.

In an earlier time, perhaps half of the island was covered with forests. Over the centuries, however, planters cleared much of the land for farming. And throughout much of Cuba's history, the most popular crop on those farms has been another immigrant plant,

*In this 19th-century illustration, an overseer and a plantation owner survey a field of tobacco while the workers pick tobacco leaves. Today, Havanas, as the Cuban cigars are called, are an important export for the country's economy.*

sugarcane. Introduced to Cuba in 1498, today sugarcane is the principal crop nationwide.

Other crops rank far behind sugarcane both in quantities grown and in value to the nation's economy, but they are, nevertheless, indispensable as food for Cubans and as exports to other nations. A variety of citrus and tropical fruits, such as oranges, grapefruit, pineapples, bananas, lemons, and limes, are grown. Cuban farmers also raise more exotic items: mangoes, guavas, coconuts, papayas (a yellow melon-like fruit, also called fruta bomba), plantains (a tropical fruit related to the banana), and avocados (also called alligator pears).

Several crops are grown mainly for domestic consumption, including rice, beans, maize, cassava, potatoes, sweet potatoes, and tomatoes. Coffee, though still a minor crop, is also cultivated.

Spanish settlers introduced domesticated cattle to Cuba early in the island's recorded history. For many years the preferred breed was a humpbacked ox, native to Asia, called the zebu, prized for its resistance to tropical heat and ticks. In recent years, farmers and ranchers have introduced new breeds of cattle and have crossbred them with the zebu in an attempt to improve meat and milk yields. Many Cuban farmers also raise swine and chickens.

Sportfishing is a popular recreation along Cuba's coasts and has attracted fishermen from around the world. The warm seas off Cuba support many species of fish, including snapper, tarpon, mutton-fish, *emperador*, or swordfish, bonito, barracuda, mackerel, marlin, and several varieties of *tiburón*, or shark. The *tortuga*, or sea turtle, and a marine mammal called the manatee, or sea cow, are both protected by law because of overhunting in the past.

Oysters, crabs, shrimp, crawfish, and a spiny lobster called the langosta are all harvested for food. Some of these creatures are even raised on aquatic farms, and the Cuban government has instituted extensive fish-farming in an attempt to satisfy domestic food requirements. However, much of the heavy commercial fishing done

*A variety of tropical fish live on the coral reefs that surround the island of Cuba and that are abundant in the warm waters of the Caribbean. Coral, an invertebrate organism, secretes calcium carbonate, which becomes its stony skeleton; the skeleton, in turn, provides the framework for coral reefs and the environment for many other kinds of sea life, including algae, plants, snails, and fish.*

by the nation's fleet is undertaken far from Cuba, in the northern Atlantic Ocean and even in the Pacific, where great fish such as the *atún* or *albacora* (tuna) can be found.

Lovers of nature rightfully value Cuba's wildlife not for hunting or fishing but simply to admire. The island is home to many species of tropical birds—some brilliantly colored—such as the flamingo, Cuban parrot, Cuban trogon, tody, pygmy owl, and shearwater. Many migratory birds also make the island their home in winter months, returning to North America in the spring. However, one winged creature of Cuba is universally detested: the mosquito. At one time, this bloodsucking insect was feared as a spreader of malaria and yellow fever. Through preventive measures, these infectious diseases have gradually been eliminated from many areas, but the mosquito remains an abundant and annoying pest.

*A 1794 engraving depicts a Taíno cacique, or chief, addressing Christopher Columbus and his men when they arrived on the island. The Taíno Indians were the people who gave Cuba its name, which means "central place."*

# 3

# Settlement and Slavery

The first settlers of Cuba were the Ciboney and Guanahacabibe, Indian peoples who originated in Central or South America and migrated by canoe to the Antilles, perhaps as long ago as 3,500 B.C. The two groups hunted, fished, and gathered foodstuffs to survive. They lived in scattered locations across Cuba, but mainly along the coast and in caves.

These two tribes were gradually displaced by a third, the Taíno, who came to Cuba around A.D. 1100 from what is now the island of Hispaniola. By 1492, when Christopher Columbus arrived, the Taíno occupied most of the island, especially the southeast, whereas the other tribes were limited to the far west. Today the westernmost peninsula of the island is still known as the Peninsula de Guanahacabibes. (In 1920, a number of pre-Columbian artifacts were found in a cavern, now called the Cave of Indians, or Cueva de los Indios, in the Viñales Valley, west of Havana. The term *pre-Columbian* refers to all events and objects in the Americas preceding the arrival of Columbus.)

The Taíno are also referred to as Arawak, for they were one of a number of South American tribes that spoke a language called

*The Taíno lived in bohíos, huts made of bamboo and palm fronds. This 1897 photograph depicts a bohío in a rural area; even today bohíos can be found in some Cuban villages.*

Arawakan. It was the Taíno who gave Cuba the name it still bears, which means "central place."

The Taíno were a more advanced people than the tribes they had displaced. They not only hunted, fished, and gathered food but also cultivated crops such as maize, cassava, beans, and tobacco. Farming enabled them to maintain a stable society, and they lived in permanent villages, residing in huts called *bohíos* made of bamboo and palm fronds. Even today the shacks of many rural Cubans are still called bohíos and are often constructed of these materials. Adept with tools, the Taíno wove fishnets, carved fishhooks, spun cloth from cotton, and hollowed out large canoes from tree trunks. They also made pottery, fashioned gourds into cooking and drinking vessels, and built furniture with palm branches.

Columbus spoke highly of the Taíno people he met and also noted that they told of a neighboring people "of whom they were very much afraid . . . they could not talk to these people because they would be eaten." Columbus misunderstood them to be called Caniba—the proper name of this invading tribe was, in fact, the Carib. The word *Caribbean* is derived from their name, and the term *cannibal* from the mangled version.

By the end of the 15th century, the Carib had gained control of the Lesser Antilles and had begun to raid Cuba and the other large islands, inciting terror among the Taíno by their ferocity. Columbus was forced to battle the Carib at every encounter.

## Conquistadores

The advent of Spanish civilization proved disastrous for both the Carib and the Taíno. Columbus's sincere desire to peacefully convert them to European ways was shared by few of his successors. During the 1500s, the Taíno underwent a state of siege by the *conquistadores* (Spanish conquerors); those who survived were then enslaved to work the gold mines and tobacco plantations. Furthermore, the Spanish had unwittingly brought with them various diseases, such as smallpox, measles, and influenza. These illnesses were common, although rarely fatal, among Europeans, but the Indians lacked immunity to the diseases and died in epidemic numbers.

By the end of the 16th century, the Indian population of Cuba was virtually nonexistent, and as early as 1524 the Spaniards began to import Africans to take the Indians' place. Most of the Africans were from the Bantu, Congolese, Dahoman, Mandingo, and Yoruba tribes of west Africa. The few Indian survivors married into African slave or Spanish society; and with the merging of their bloodlines, the island's first peoples vanished. Today Cuba, unlike Mexico and most of Central and South America, has no natives of distinctively Indian or mestizo (mixed Indian and Spanish) ancestry.

The Spanish colonization of Cuba started in 1511. Under royal commission, Diego Velásquez, a rich planter from Hispaniola, sailed forth with a company of about 300 conquistadores to begin settling the island. They founded the country's first permanent Spanish settlement, Baracoa, near the island's southeastern tip. Within five years several more towns were established across the island, including Sancti Spíritus, Puerto Príncipe (later renamed Camagüey), and Santiago. (The former is usually referred to as Santiago de Cuba to distinguish it from Santiago, Chile.) Havana was also founded at this time, but authorities twice relocated the city to more favorable sites, finally deciding on its present location on the northwest coast.

In the early 1500s, Pope Alexander VI declared the Spanish king the secular head of the Catholic church in his country and all its colonies. Given control over church finances and the appointment of church officials, the Spanish crown was able to turn the clergy into agents of the government. As the conquistadores advanced, cathedrals were among the first buildings to be erected in new towns. Catholic religious orders, such as the Jesuits and Dominicans, became important landowners and also ran the school sys-

*The University of Havana was founded by the Dominicans in 1728. The Catholic clergy became important to Cuba as a means of transmitting Spanish art and culture to the people.*

tem. (Cuba's foremost center of learning, the University of Havana, was founded by the Dominicans in 1728.) The clergy became a conduit through which Spanish religion, art, and culture came to Cuba.

## Peninsulares and Criollos

Political authority in the American territories was almost completely in the hands of people born in Spain and appointed by either the Crown or its councils. These people, called *peninsulares*, formed a select ruling class whose allegiance was to Spain rather than to one colony. At their head was the colonial governor, known by his military title of *captain general*. Those Spaniards born and raised in the Americas were called *criollos*; however prominent they might become in business or agriculture, they exercised little control over government affairs except at the lowest level.

The political power of the peninsulares meant that for many years the island's affairs were actually a reflection of Spain's: Spanish wars and Spanish alliances in faraway Europe determined Cuban political behavior. The native criollos came to resent and, ultimately, oppose, the outside rule over them.

The Spanish began to neglect Cuba when vast wealth started to pour out of the mainland with the conquests of Mexico by Hernán Cortés in the 1520s and of Peru by Francisco Pizarro in the 1530s. By 1535, Spain regarded the island primarily as a port through which the mother country's naval traffic could be routed for repairs and other services. By 1589, Havana had become the Cuban capital because of its excellent natural harbor, and authorities rapidly built it up to fortify it against attacks by enemies. (Parts of the old fortress can still be seen today in Old Havana.)

Although Spain had a firm grip on Mexico and much of Central and South America, England and France fought over North America. At the same time, these countries sought to gain a foothold in the West Indies and occasionally captured treasure-laden ships sailing from South America to Spain. Throughout the colonial era, Spain would switch alliances between England and France—first fighting one, then the other.

Some of Spain's poorly conceived economic policies actually contributed to this combative state of affairs. The Spanish crown attempted to impose upon its American colonies a trade monopoly—that is, the colonies could send their raw materials to, and receive trade goods from, Spain alone. Spain received much more in colonial resources than it could supply in manufactured goods. Many discontented criollos, unable to get the supplies they needed, soon began to trade illegally, an activity that led to extensive smuggling, official corruption, and an increase in international hostilities.

## Pirates

The 17th century was a kind of golden age of piracy in the West Indies. Pirates thrived on raids against ships and coastal towns and then on the illegal trade in the goods they had stolen. Pirate communities often established themselves on uncharted cays of the larger islands. Spanish forces sailed out of Cuba in sporadic raids against buccaneer communities but without much success.

By the end of the 1600s, legitimate French settlement had become so entrenched on Hispaniola that Spain officially relinquished the western third of the island, which became Saint Domingue, forerunner of the nation of Haiti. In the meantime—in 1655—British naval forces, with the help of pirates, had seized Spain's island of Jamaica.

Political authorities in Saint Domingue and Jamaica had no control over the buccaneers, and the two colonial governments chose not to hinder them in their crimes. Jamaica's Port Royal soon became a haven for hundreds of buccaneers. Among them was Henry Morgan, a Welsh-born sailor who had come to the West Indies in his teens and quickly earned a reputation as one of the most ruthless pirates in the region. In 1668, the Cuban town of Puerto Príncipe became prey to one of Morgan's most notorious raids.

Piracy would persist to some degree until the 19th century. But it decreased greatly beginning in the early 18th century, largely because of shifts in government alliances and attitudes that left the buccaneers politically friendless.

## Trade

At the beginning of the 18th century, England and Spain were at war again, in a conflict called the War of the Spanish Succession. Once again, Spain and its allies were defeated. In 1713, in the Treaty of Utrecht, Spain was forced to relax the trade monopoly its held over Cuba and its other colonies.

Until this time, Cubans outside of coastal towns had worked primarily at cattle ranching and the lumber business; the tobacco industry also surged as smoking caught on in Europe. Sugarcane had been introduced to the Caribbean by Columbus back in 1498, but only with the new influx of African slaves could it become a major Cuban crop, for—like cotton in the American South—its harvesting required widespread, exhausting physical labor. Planters found that sugarcane grew easily on Cuban soil and that it

*Slaves cut and load sugarcane at the plantation of Las Cañas. Columbus introduced sugarcane to the Caribbean in 1498, but the industry required vast amounts of cheap labor to become profitable. Planters began to import African slaves to do the backbreaking work, and sugar soon became the country's major crop.*

required less care than the delicate tobacco plant. Soon sugar's importance to the island's economy surpassed that of tobacco, and Cuba's slave population grew with it.

In 1756, England and Spain were drawn into fighting through their opposing alliances with other warring countries in Europe. In 1762, British forces seized Havana, and through it, they effectively controlled the whole island. Although British rule was to last less than a year, it would affect Cuba profoundly.

Military occupation opened up Cuban trade with Britain's global empire, especially its American colonies. For a brief time, the island's economy boomed. Upon winning the Seven Years' War, however, England agreed in 1763 to withdraw from Cuba in exchange for possession of Florida. Spanish economic control returned to Cuba along with the Spanish flag.

## Revolt in the Colonies

During the American War of Independence, Spain actually sided with the rebel colonies. In an attempt to damage its old enemy, England, the Spanish crown allowed Cuba to trade with the United States starting in 1776, and in 1779 it followed France in declaring war on Britain. However, after the United States finally achieved lasting victory in 1783, Spain cut off the new nation's trade with Cuba. By this gesture the Crown showed its disapproval of colonial revolts against monarchies.

A much greater challenge to the idea of royal authority arose in 1789 with the French Revolution. Through acts such as the storming of the Bastille and through public documents such as the Declaration of the Rights of Man, French revolutionaries had an enormous influence on Europe and the Americas. The ideals of Liberty, Equality, [and] Fraternity—the motto of the French movement—were widely seen as justifying the violent overthrow of established regimes everywhere.

*In 1791, Toussaint L'Ouverture (center) leads a revolt of slaves in Saint Domingue. The revolt soon turned into a war for independence, and in 1804, the French colony declared itself the free nation of Haiti.*

As the 1700s drew to a close, France's greatest possession in the Caribbean was Saint Domingue. The French colony enjoyed even more success than Cuba as a sugar producer because it held a much greater number of slaves—nearly a half million. Saint Domingue had already seen several unsuccessful slave rebellions in the 1700s, and news of the French Revolution threw the colony into further agitation. In 1791, Saint Domingue's people of color united to bring about a massive slave revolt that soon turned into a war for self-governance. For more than a decade, the entire island of Hispaniola was immersed in bloody chaos, and in 1804 the colony declared itself the independent nation of Haiti.

The long anarchy preceding Haiti's birth affected Cuba from the very beginning. Many who lived on the island of Hispaniola fled the surrounding violence and havoc for the safety of Cuba. Some brought with them the advanced technical knowledge and skill that had made Saint Domingue a first-rate sugar producer. And the new nation they had escaped lay in ruins, giving Cuba even greater impetus to devote itself chiefly to the profitable sugar industry. Finally, the Haitian revolution produced in Cuba an opposite reaction, encouraging social rigidity and blind obedience to Spain because Cubans feared a similar upheaval in their own country.

*Luis Rodolfo Miranda, adjutant of Major General Calixto García, waves the Cuban flag at the battle of Santiago de Cuba during the War for Independence in 1898.*

# 4

# Rebellion

By the end of the 1700s, the French Revolution had collapsed from its own violence, leaving in its wake a military dictatorship under the popular general Napoléon Bonaparte. In 1808, Emperor Napoléon proclaimed his brother, Joseph Bonaparte, the king of Spain. The presence of a Frenchman on the Spanish throne, though temporary, gave Spain's American colonies an excuse to cut ties with their mother country. Beginning in 1810, each Spanish possession on the mainland fought for, and eventually won, its independence. By 1825, only Cuba and Puerto Rico retained colonial status.

In Cuba, ranching and farming—especially the cultivation of sugar and tobacco—prospered, and the slave population grew. By the mid-1800s, the island became home to about 1.5 million people: 750,000 criollos, 250,000 free blacks and mulattoes, and 500,000 slaves.

Military rule under a captain general continued; Cubans had no voice in their government, no freedom of speech or right to assemble. Although they denied Cubans political freedom, the Spanish authorities did concede some economic freedom by ending their trade monopoly. However, they imposed a high tariff (a tax) on all goods traded internationally.

One of Cuba's trading partners was the United States. With settlers pushing ever westward across North America, U.S. leaders became increasingly aware of Cuba's strategic location beyond the Gulf of Mexico. U.S. officials actually felt little threat from the declining Spanish Empire, but they feared that Cuba might some-day be captured by a hostile nation and then used as a military stronghold from which to attack the United States. This concern was magnified when, during the War of 1812, Spain allowed British warships to dock at Cuban ports.

As a result, the United States made repeated attempts throughout much of the 1800s to purchase Cuba from Spain so that it might be politically annexed. These proposals were supported by some in-fluential citizens in both the United States and Cuba. In the United States, annexation was supported primarily by those interested in national defense, by businessmen who hoped the move would be good for commerce, and by slave owners. Southern slave owners wanted Cuba to be a "slave state" to strengthen their own political hand against the industrialized, abolitionist North.

Many slave owners in Cuba also favored annexation. As the desire for nationhood spread among the Cuban people, slave owners feared that a war of independence against Spain would inevitably lead to a vast slave uprising such as the one in Haiti: Annexation to the United States as a slave state would preserve their way of life. Other Cuban patriots supported annexation because they saw political union with the thriving, democratic country as an intermediate step toward long-term independence. Spain, how-ever, steadfastly refused to give up its colony.

A few Americans actually wanted to declare war on Spain and forcibly seize Cuba, but this action would have been contrary to official U.S. policy as set forth in the Monroe Doctrine. This policy, established by President James Monroe in 1823, was largely a

*A 1912 painting depicts President James Monroe (standing) expressing his policy oppos-*
*ing European influence in the Western Hemisphere. The 1823 pronouncement is now*
*known as the Monroe Doctrine; it included a U.S. pledge of noninterference in existing*
*European colonies such as Cuba.*

warning that European nations should stay out of the Americas and
that the United States would view any intervention in the region as
an aggressive act. At the same time, however, Monroe stated that
the United States would not upset the status quo; it would not
interfere with those few colonies in the Americas, such as Cuba, that
were still held by European nations. This pledge of noninterference
helped keep American hands off Cuba in the early 1800s. More
important, the United States was deadlocked over the domestic
issue of slavery. Tensions over slavery finally led to the outbreak of
the American Civil War in 1861. The South's defeat in 1865 put an
end to slavery in the United States and with it any hope among
criollo planters of preserving Cuban slavery through annexation.

Despite the ominous example of the American South, Cuba
seemed to have prospered by slavery and sugar. The city of Matan-

*The city of Matanzas, founded in 1693, was an important port for the shipment of beef and pork to Spain. In the 19th century, the surrounding province was rich in farmland, and the city became the sugarcane capital of Cuba and a major slave depot.*

zas, for example, became a boomtown through its strategic bay-side location and rich farmland. Prosperous planters made the city a haven for artistic and intellectual activity, and soon Matanzas was internationally celebrated as "the Athens of Cuba." Similarly, the cities of Cienfuegos, Trinidad, and Santiago thrived on slave trading, general commerce, and agriculture.

Slave revolts in Cuba dated as far back as the early 1500s. The tensions between slaves and owners mirrored those that had grown between criollos and the peninsulares. In 1825, in response to criollo political plots, the Spanish crown had granted Cuba's captain general almost unlimited powers; for example, he was able to deport anyone he believed to be politically objectionable. Some captains general exercised this power freely, and by the mid-1800s a number of exiles had relocated to New Orleans and New York, where many worked to raise money and U.S. support for their cause.

The struggle for freedom erupted into open conflict on October 10, 1868, when Carlos Manuel de Céspedes, a rich criollo planter and lawyer, freed his slaves and, together with other landowners, led them into battle for Cuban independence in his hometown of Yara. A group of fellow rebels selected Céspedes as president of their government, and a rebel army was soon fighting under a trio of generals: Máximo Gómez, Calixto García, and Antonio Maceo.

But the rebel forces had several obstacles to overcome. For one thing, not all Cubans supported the war. Céspedes had freed his own slaves, but not all plantation owners were willing to follow suit. Most Americans sympathized with the rebels, but the U.S. government avoided involvement. Because of U.S. neutrality the United States could not sell arms to the rebels, whose lack of military supplies became a growing problem. Machetes—the long, broad knives used to cut sugarcane—became the rebels' weapons.

U.S. neutrality did not prevent some private citizens from illegally shipping arms to the rebels. At the end of October 1873, the privately owned ship *Virginius*, with a crew of nearly 150 British and American men, was captured outside of Santiago while running guns. Within a few days the Spanish military had shot 53 crew members. Only the arrival of an imposing British warship in Santiago's harbor prevented further executions. An outraged American public called for war, but the U.S. government settled for lesser measures, including Spanish compensation to the families of those who had been killed.

Under General Gómez, rebel forces had engaged in hit-and-run skirmishes rather than large battles; because supplies were scarce, Gómez decided to destroy the island's sugar mills, a tactic meant to cripple the Spanish economy.

But events conspired against the rebels. In 1874, Céspedes was killed in battle, and no successor of equal repute emerged. In the following year, Spain's domestic troubles subsided after a new king ascended the throne. By the end of 1878, Gómez was in exile in

Honduras, and the Ten Years' War (as it is now called) had con-
cluded with the Pact of Zanjón. Cuban war deaths were estimated
at 50,000, and Spanish casualties were much higher—more than
200,000.

The Cubans had lost, but the war served to advance the cause of
independence. Hostility toward Spain ran deeper than ever before,
and now a generation of fighters had learned the art of guerrilla
warfare. Many rebels went into exile in the United States and
formed a network to keep the revolution alive.

Although neither Spain nor Cuba had intended it, the Ten Years'
War also further impelled the United States to help the island with
its economy. The war had brought widespread destruction and
resulting poverty, and U.S. businessmen possessed the money and
technology for Cuba's recovery. Moreover, the European demand
for Cuban sugar had slowly been fading throughout the 19th century, and the war served to weaken it even more. By the end of the

*José Martí was held
captive at El Abra farm on
the Isle of Youth (formerly
Isle of Pines) before he was
exiled to Spain in 1870 for
his political opinions.
Martí returned to Cuba in
March 1895 to help lead
the revolutionaries and
was killed in battle in May.*

*Major General Calixto García's troops are victorious at Fort Gonfau on October 28, 1896. During the War of Independence more than 300,000 Cubans died fighting Spain.*

century the United States had become Cuba's main export market for sugar and tobacco products.

However, no matter what international links bound them, Cubans still wanted political independence. Spain had scarcely won the Ten Years' War when it faced another uprising. *La Guerra Chiquita*, or The Little War, was launched in August 1879 by several rebel leaders in defiance of the Pact of Zanjón. This time Spain moved quickly. Within a year, the uprising had been suppressed and its leaders jailed or dispersed. General Calixto García was deported to Spain and imprisoned. General Antonio Maceo went into exile in Central America. Yet another Cuban patriot was deported to Spain but soon got free and journeyed to New York: the poet José Martí.

Martí, born in Havana in 1853, was 15 years old when the Ten Years' War started. At age 17, although too young for combat action, he began voicing political opinions, which soon led to jail and deportation to Spain. Martí traveled to Mexico and Guatemala upon his release, beginning a lifelong career in journalism before The Little War led to his exile in New York. Martí worked to spread the Cuban viewpoint among U.S. citizens. He also toiled to organize his fellow exiles. He helped found the Cuban Revolutionary party and conferred with Máximo Gómez and Antonio Maceo on revolutionary strategy.

In 1886, the practice of slavery finally came to an end in Cuba. In the next decade, most Cuban exiles acknowledged the political leadership of its New York–based *junta*, or administrative council. Under the junta's direction, a new war of independence began on February 24, 1895, with the Grito de Baire (Battle Cry of Baire). Martí, Gómez, and Maceo did not actually return to the island until about a month later. Then, on May 19, 1895, Martí himself was killed in battle.

Martí's death left General Gómez as the island's most prominent revolutionary leader, just as he had been some 20 years before. Backed by Generals Maceo and García (who had been released from prison), and with Tomás Estrada Palma now heading the Cuban junta in New York, Gómez made it known that the rebels would accept nothing less than total independence for Cuba. He immediately began to destroy sugarcane fields and sugar mills.

The renewal of warfare focused international attention on Cuba, and most of the world's sympathy was clearly with the rebels.

In the United States, some of the support for the rebels was based on self-interest, because many Americans had lived on the island and owned property and businesses there. Other Americans remembered the bloody Ten Years' War—memories that were prompted by information spread by the New York junta. And the leading American newspapers, such as Joseph Pulitzer's *New York World* and William Randolph Hearst's *Morning Journal*, found that their readers responded to colorful tales of the Cuban conflict.

Some Cubans supported a U.S. takeover. In June 1896, for example, more than 100 prominent Cubans joined together to request U.S. intervention and annexation. These men were alarmed by both the rebels' strategy of destruction and by Spain's replacement of the ruling captain general with a new leader, Valeriano

*Reconcentrados, the people who were forced to live in the prison camps that Valeriano Weyler had established, wait for the distribution of food during the war. Thousands died of starvation and disease.*

Weyler, who had a fearsome reputation. Weyler matched the rebels' policy of destruction by burning food crops in the rebel-held areas. He also forced civilians to move into prison camps. Weyler's policy was called *reconcentración*, or "bringing together," and thousands of *reconcentrados*—those who had to live in the camps—died of starvation and disease in these terrible camps. More than 300,000 Cubans (out of a total population of only 1.5 million) died during the War of Independence. Weyler's actions negated earlier rebel gains, and in December 1896 the independence movement suffered a terrible blow when General Antonio Maceo was killed in western Cuba.

One month earlier, William McKinley had been elected president of the United States. McKinley had long expressed his desire for regional peace and Cuban independence. He also made clear to

*The wreckage of the USS* Maine *lies partly submerged in Havana's harbor after the ship mysteriously blew up in February 1898. The blast, which most Americans had attributed to foul play on the part of Spain, thrust the United States into war.*

Spain his displeasure at the threat to American interests in Cuba and Weyler's murderous reconcentración policy.

In 1898, Spain decided to replace Weyler with another captain general. Worried about how this change might affect the island, the U.S. diplomatic envoy in Cuba requested that a battleship be sent to defend American citizens. That ship, the USS *Maine*, was docked in Havana's harbor on the evening of February 15, 1898, when it was hit by a series of explosions. More than two-thirds of the crew died in the sinking battleship.

Spain denied responsibility for the blast, and no guilt was ever assigned. But the death of American sailors angered their fellow

*(continued on page 57)*

# SCENES OF
# CUBA

Overleaf: *A colonial mansion in Camagüey (formerly called Puerto Príncipe) is embellished with* tinajones, *designed after the large-bellied, wide-mouthed wine and oil jars of Spain. The jars were used for collecting rainwater because the province had little underground water. The number and size of the jars that a family owned often indicated its economic position in the community.*

*Cuba's Central Highway, also called the Cuban Thruway, is state owned and runs from Santiago de Cuba to Pinar del Río.*

*The Great Theater of Havana
(also called the García Lorca
Theater) was built in 1837 and
is the site for performances by
the National Ballet, Opera, and
Light Opera companies.*

*Varadero Beach, with its shimmering white sand and turquoise water, became a popular resort in the 1930s. Today, new hotels and villas have been built in the area, and the resort city is home to more than 15,000 people.*

*The Basílica El Cobre, where the shrine of the patron
saint Virgen de la Caridad del Cobre is located, is
Cuba's only basilica and is situated in the foothills of
the Sierra Maestra. El Cobre, which is northwest of
Santiago de Cuba, is named for the first open copper
mine in the Americas.*

*Coral and tropical sea creatures live in the warm
waters surrounding Cuba. The island is famous
around the world for its spectacular scuba diving
and other water sports.*

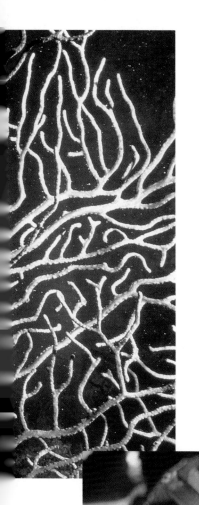

The water hyacinth, a native
flower of Cuba, grows abundantly
in lakes and streams, often
clogging major waterways
with its floating roots.

*The Archaeological Mural on one of the outcroppings in*
*Viñales Valley depicts prehistoric snails, a marine monster,*
*and animals that first inhabited the area. The mural was*
*painted from 1959 to 1962 under the direction of Leovigildo*
*González, who was a student of the famous Mexican artist*
*Diego Rivera.*

(continued from page 48)

citizens in a way that Cuban casualties could not. And, unlike the *Virginius* of a generation earlier, the *Maine* had been an official U.S. vessel on a formal visit. Urged on by screaming headlines and by the popular slogan Remember the *Maine!*, the U.S. Congress in late April declared war on Spain. Cuba's War of Independence had suddenly become what is now sometimes called the Spanish-Cuban-American War.

U.S. forces achieved victory in Cuba in one summer. An American naval blockade had stopped Spanish troops and supplies from reaching the island. After U.S. Marines took Guantánamo Bay, a series of battles ensued, most notably at El Caney and San Juan Hill (Kettle Hill). By late August, the fighting was over. In December 1898, under the Treaty of Paris, Spain gave up all claim to Cuba.

U.S. military forces did not immediately withdraw from the island; nevertheless, annexation had been rejected—when Congress declared war, it had also passed the Teller Amendment, which disavowed any permanent U.S. jurisdiction over Cuba. In 1899, as

*In 1898, President William McKinley (fifth from right) watches the signing of the Treaty of Paris, the peace protocol in which Spain gave up all claim to Cuba.*

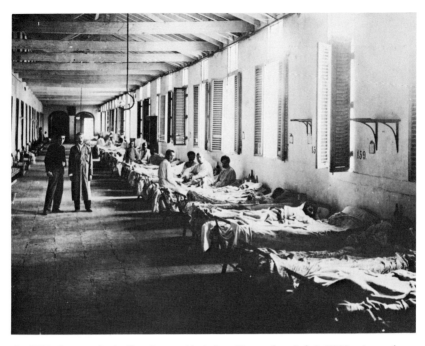

*An 1899 photograph of yellow fever patients in a Havana hospital. In 1900, a team of doctors, including the Cuban doctor Carlos Juan Finlay, conducted tests and were successful in finding a treatment for the disease.*

a compromise, a provisional military government was set up. This arrangement would last until 1902.

The provisional government worked to rebuild the war-devastated island, to construct schools, to train teachers (two-thirds or more of the people were illiterate), and to restore public services. Perhaps most important, however, was its attack upon the disease yellow fever. This often-fatal virus was at that time a common killer in the tropics. A Cuban doctor, Carlos Juan Finlay, had been the first to suggest that mosquitoes carried the disease. In 1900, a team of Cuban and American physicians, including Walter Reed and Aristides Agramonte, conducted tests to study the illness, its transmission, and methods for its control. At the end of these experiments, health workers were able to treat the disease, and using similar control measures, they found an effective treatment for malaria.

The Cubans had fought and died for independence. The longer governance by the United States continued, the greater Cuban resentment grew. And, back in the United States, taxpayers resented the millions of dollars being spent to maintain the occupation. In the summer of 1900, the provisional government began to hold local elections, followed by balloting for a constitutional convention. An assembly of delegates met and hammered out a constitution by February 1901.

To ease Americans' concerns about Cuba's political stability, the U.S. Congress passed the Platt Amendment, which established limited U.S. authority over Cuba. The amendment was to give the United States the privilege "to intervene for the preservation of Cuban independence, [and] the maintenance of a government adequate for the protection of life, property, and individual liberty." Among its other provisions, the Platt Amendment allowed the United States to buy or lease Cuban land for naval bases. (One such base, acquired through a later treaty, is still leased today at Guantánamo Bay.)

Congress's action concerning Cuba stemmed from the long-standing American concern about Cuba's strategic location. But another issue had also arisen: plans for the Panama Canal. Construction of the actual canal did not begin until 1904, but U.S. officials had been negotiating for years to create a Central American waterway connecting the Atlantic and Pacific oceans. Possession of the canal would be vital to America's defense in a war, and to ensure its safety, the United States wanted political stability throughout the Caribbean.

Most Cubans were angered by the Platt Amendment and saw it as an intrusion. President McKinley personally assured a visiting Cuban commission that its "sole purpose" was to permit intervention "in order to prevent foreign attacks against . . . the Cuban republic, or when there may exist a true state of anarchy within the republic." In June 1901, the Cubans added the provisions of the Platt Amendment to their new constitution.

Elections held in 1901 gave the Republic of Cuba its first president, and U.S. forces quickly withdrew from the island. Tomás Estrada Palma, a veteran of the Ten Years' War and former head of the Cuban junta, took office in May 1902. His tranquil first term was marked by further reconstruction of the nation.

The next election, however, showed the defects of the Platt Amendment. Estrada Palma had a spotless reputation for personal honesty, but in 1905 his opponents accused his political party of stealing election votes through fraud, bribery, and threats. Attempts at compromise failed, and a few months later the opposition began an armed rebellion. Both the rebels and the government appealed to the United States for help. In September 1906, Estrada Palma decided to resign from office and thus forced the United States to install a second provisional government, backed by troops to restore order. This government, under diplomat Charles Magoon, lasted a little more than two years and departed in January 1909 after overseeing new elections. But until the Platt Amendment was finally terminated in 1934, American diplomatic intervention would continue under its provisions.

America's political view of Cuba was further complicated by financial involvement. Economic problems brought about by World War I put many Cuban planters deeply in debt, leading to further U.S. buyouts in the sugar industry. Because Cubans continued to rely on a single crop for their welfare, their dependence on it grew ever greater. Rather than diversify their economy by developing a variety of industries, the Cubans essentially sold sugar to the rest of the world and imported everything they needed. Their biggest customer was the United States, and its technological superiority soon allowed America to dominate some basic Cuban utilities, such as the telephone company.

Many Cubans went to work for U.S. businesses rather than starting their own. Others went to work for their government, which failed to push for national self-sufficiency. Instead of encouraging private enterprise, the government concentrated on public works programs, such as the construction of roads, schools, and hospitals. These programs employed Cubans, but they required more tax money to maintain.

As a result, no strong, business-owning middle class developed to stabilize Cuban politics. Such a class would have possessed a personal stake in the island's domestic stability. Instead, society was increasingly divided into small, contending groups. Three factions in particular had a strong interest in public affairs: the government workers themselves; a loose alliance of students and scholars, mostly at the University of Havana; and the Cuban army. All three of these groups played a role in the career of Gerardo Machado, Cuba's first *caudillo*, or military dictator.

In 1924, Machado, a skillful politician, was elected president. He enjoyed great popularity at first and was able to push important laws through the legislature. Machado continued the extensive public works programs of earlier presidents, increased funds for the Cuban army, and placed his followers in important military positions. He was reelected in 1928, and soon after, in 1929, a worldwide depression put many Cubans out of work.

In order to continue his programs, Machado raised taxes and borrowed huge sums of money from overseas. This kept government workers employed and on his side, but ultimately it hurt the economy even more. Protests soared as people demanded relief. Machado's response was simple: violent repression. The government censored the press, employed secret police to jail or kill labor union leaders, used the army to prevent public meetings, and shut down the University of Havana to silence student dissent. But Machado's actions led only to equally vehement retaliation. Many student activists were already disenchanted because of government fraud and corruption, and some radicals now embraced terrorism as an appropriate means to fight Machado.

In 1933, Franklin Roosevelt took office as president of the United States and appointed Sumner Welles his ambassador to Cuba. Welles quickly made himself a power broker in island politics. He held meetings with various opposition groups, arranged negotiations, and even made suggestions on who should succeed Machado.

That summer, a series of strikes paralyzed the island. Army officers, fearing that U.S. troops might at last invade Cuba, began to urge their caudillo to step down. With a military revolt impending, Machado finally fled into exile in the Bahamas.

In early September 1933, a new and virtually unknown president emerged: Dr. Ramón Grau, a University of Havana professor. Grau was respected for his anti-Machado activities and was backed by a coalition of student activists and army members. Numerous reforms took place during Grau's brief time in office: Women received the right to vote, a minimum-wage law was passed, and a ministry of labor was created. By early 1934, however, Grau was exiled after a power struggle, and yet another president, Carlos Mendieta, was installed. But the source of Mendieta's power was the army alone, which was commanded by a man named Fulgencio Batista.

Military power had been the basis of Spain's control over Cuba for centuries, and in the 1920s Machado had revived its use in daily government. This tradition now expanded under Batista. Soldiers held many government posts that were formerly occupied by civilians; in the countryside, army officers supervised schools and public health clinics. Although civilian presidents continued in office, the army exerted much influence from behind the scenes.

*Fulgencio Batista, commander of the Cuban army, supported the presidencies of Ramón Grau and Carlos Mendieta. In 1940, Batista himself ran for president and won. During Batista's term in office, government corruption soared.*

Batista, a mulatto born of poor parents, had joined the army as a private, rising to the rank of sergeant. In 1933, he had led a mutiny by enlisted officers that had brought about the presidencies of Ramón Grau and, soon afterward, Carlos Mendieta.

Cuba's economy slowly began to recover in the mid-1930s. Dozens of resort hotels and gambling casinos were built during this era, and the island became known in Europe and America as a tourists' paradise. The Cuban political scene also improved. In May 1934, U.S. officials acknowledged the stability of Mendieta's government by terminating the Platt Amendment—to the great joy of most Cubans. A second constitutional convention was called, and a new constitution was ratified in 1940. Among its provisions, this progressive document recognized the right of workers to unionize, bargain, and strike for better working conditions.

In the fall of 1940, Batista ran for president. His opponent was former president Grau, who had returned from exile to form a new political organization, the Auténtico (Authentic) party. In what is believed to have been a generally honest election, Batista won.

Batista left office in 1944, having dominated Cuban political life for a decade. He retired a rich man, for political graft had thrived during his term, as it would under his successors. In the next election, Ramón Grau defeated a Batista-backed candidate to become president again. But many Cubans were disappointed by Grau's failure to enact reforms such as those passed during his first term in office. Grau's successor, Carlos Prío, proved to be a more effective politician. A member of the Auténtico party, Prío had entered politics as a leader of the anti-Machado student movement. Prío's term was marred by the corruption and outbursts of radical violence that had plagued earlier presidents, but he achieved important reforms. He oversaw the creation of a new national banking system and enforced closer safeguards over government spending. During Prío's presidency, Cuban-owned companies at last began to make inroads where previously only foreign firms had existed.

This imperfect but authentic democracy came to an abrupt end in March 1952, when—shortly before new elections—Fulgencio Batista, who had emerged from retirement to seize power, led a military revolt and overthrew the government. He promptly suspended constitutional guarantees, banned all political parties, and closed down the legislature.

At first Batista encountered little opposition—the army uprising had taken place without bloodshed. But as soon as he was in power, he found he had little real support outside the army, and he could not bribe his more idealistic opponents.

The first violent assault on his regime occurred on July 26, 1953. Approximately 125 Cubans attacked a large army base at Moncada, near Santiago. The raid failed completely. The rebels who survived or who were not captured fled, including their leader, a 26-year-old lawyer named Fidel Castro.

Until that day, Castro had been a minor political figure to most of the Cuban public. Born in 1926, the son of a rich Spanish planter, Castro attended exclusive private schools and then studied law at the University of Havana, where he became involved in radical political groups. The ambitious young Castro also became a follower of Eduardo Chibás, a founder of the Ortodoxo (Orthodox) party and a popular senator. Chibás was widely admired for his rousing speeches; however, in 1951 he committed suicide. Castro's own political career was stifled the following year when Batista came to power and canceled elections. It was then that Castro formed the group that in 1953 attacked the Moncada barracks.

Castro was himself a fiery speaker. After the failed attack on Moncada, the army caught Castro a few days later, and he was put on trial. He made a historic speech in his defense that lasted two hours: He denounced Batista, defended his actions, and set forth a moderate political program that included a return to national rule under the 1940 constitution. Although the speech was not widely publicized at the time, it would later be published as *History Will Absolve Me*, and it would become a famous manifesto.

Castro was imprisoned on the Isle of Pines until May 1955, when Batista, under public pressure, granted amnesty to all political prisoners. Castro denounced the dictator in a number of public speeches and newspaper articles before leaving for Mexico. There he and his fellow revolutionaries trained in combat tactics for many months. Castro was assisted in these maneuvers by a new friend, Ernesto "Che" Guevara, a 27-year-old doctor from Argentina. Guevara, a revolutionary, would later write a book on the practice of guerrilla warfare. His talents would prove invaluable, for in December 1956, Castro and his men (including Guevara and Castro's brother Raúl) returned to Cuba to wage war against

*Fidel Castro (center), leader of Cuba's revolutionaries, and his senior commanders
prepare their strategy to overthrow Batista's regime in 1957. Among the rebel leaders
in the Sierra Maestra camp are Ernesto "Che" Guevara (second from left) and Castro's
brother Raúl (center foreground).*

Batista's government. The revolutionaries used the Sierra Maestra
as the base for their operation.

In the final years of Batista's reign, his secret police tortured and
killed more than 25,000 people in an attempt to stop the network of
student and citizen protest. Meanwhile, Castro's forces were busy
in the countryside: They destroyed sugar mills, burned crops, cut
telephone lines, and occasionally fought army troops. Violence
increased constantly, and some of Batista's soldiers began to defect
to the rebels.

In the United States, officials reacted sharply as they saw Cuba turning into a police state. By late 1957, the United States took steps to start an arms embargo—that is, all sales of weapons were prohibited—against the Cuban government, further undermining Batista's stability.

Batista, on the offense, launched an attack against the rebel army. Batista's drive, which started in May 1958, turned into a disaster for the Cuban army. The rebels knew the mountain terrain far better than their pursuers and consistently eluded them while inflicting much damage.

Growing steadily in numbers, the rebel army now began to take its fight out of the mountains and into the cities. In December, they captured the major city of Santa Clara, and Batista's status as a national ruler collapsed. On January 1, 1959, he boarded a plane for the Dominican Republic, leaving Cuba for good.

*On January 1, 1979, Fidel Castro addresses the National Assembly during the celebration of the 20th anniversary of his regime.*

# 5

# Cuba Under Castro

In 1959, the new leaders of Cuba were young and inexperienced in the area of government administration. When Fidel Castro and his men entered Havana as heroes, they were filled with idealism. The first provisional government, which was to run Cuba until elections could be held, was set up immediately, and Castro selected many moderates with anti-Batista records for key positions. The first measures taken by the government were reform-related; it reduced rents by almost 50 percent and established new wage levels. With the enactment of the Agrarian Reform Law in May 1959, all land that had been owned by Batista and his supporters was confiscated, and the size of farms was limited to a maximum of 1,000 acres.

In April 1959, Castro had postponed elections on the grounds that Cuba was poor and "real democracy is not possible for hungry people." (Food rationing began in the early 1960s for the first time in the country's history and continues today.)

The 1940 constitution was never reestablished. Instead, government began to be administered through Cuba's small but well-organized Popular Socialist party (PSP), the nation's Communist party. Castro had never been a PSP member, but his brother Raúl—

soon named as head of the armed forces—had been a member of the Communist Youth while at the University of Havana. Raúl served as a link between Fidel and the Soviet-oriented PSP, and the new regime began informal relations with the Soviet Union almost immediately. As early as February 1959, Castro announced plans to sell part of the country's sugar crop to the USSR. (Relations between the two nations had been severed under Batista.) In February 1960, Soviet deputy premier Anastas Mikoyan visited the island, and a $100 million economic-aid agreement was concluded—the first of many to come.

In the spring of 1960, the Cuban government began to nationalize all sugar plantations, refineries, factories, and utilities, barring all foreigners from ownership. As a result of the new government's nationalization policy, American investors suffered major losses, and the U.S. government retaliated in July 1960 by canceling planned purchases of Cuban sugar. President Eisenhower also broke off diplomatic relations with Cuba in January 1961, after Castro demanded that all but a handful of staff at the U.S. embassy in Havana leave the country within 48 hours. By February 1962, the United States had imposed a complete embargo against Cuba that is still in effect today.

Foreign companies, however, were not the only ones affected by nationalization. In October 1960, some 400 large Cuban-owned companies were declared to be the property of the state. At about the same time, all private and religious schools were turned into state institutions. Farmland had already been affected by new laws confiscating large estates for redistribution to those with little property. Nationalization would escalate until, in March 1968, Castro declared even small businesses, from beauty parlors to hot dog stands, government property. Almost every Cuban became a government employee.

One of the first Cuban industries to fall under government control was the media. Soon after the rebel victory, all newspapers, magazines, radio broadcasts, and television programs reflected official policy. Fidel Castro himself immediately began to use radio and TV as tools by which to influence public thought. His love of speechmaking has been much in evidence on Cuba's radio and television networks.

In September 1960, Castro created a nationwide network of "vigilance groups," called Committees for the Defense of the Revolution (CDRs). CDR members were authorized to keep watch on their neighbors and report "suspicious" conduct or opinions to the authorities.

The response to some of Castro's more repressive laws and takeovers of business was an unparalleled wave of emigration from Cuba. Throughout 1959 and 1960, tens of thousands of people fled the island each month. Many were doctors, lawyers, businessmen and other professionals who left behind their homes and possessions to begin life anew elsewhere. Most resettled in the United States, especially in southern Florida. During these years, the city of Miami became home to Cubans in exile, particularly a section of town that became known as "Little Havana."

On April 17, 1961, an armed force of about 1,400 exiles attempted to make a surprise landing at Cuba's Bay of Pigs (called Playa Girón by the Cubans), on the southern coast about 50 miles (80 kilometers) east of Cienfuegos. The exiles hoped to set up a rebel government and incite a general uprising against the Castro regime. Although no U.S. military forces took part in the invasion, the U.S. Central Intelligency Agency (CIA) had trained and armed the fighters.

The operation was a total failure, however, thanks to lack of secrecy, last-minute plan changes, and lack of popular support. Within a few days, the Cuban military had killed or captured the entire exile force. Castro's victory gave a tremendous boost to his popularity at home.

After the Bay of Pigs triumph, Castro aligned his government even more closely with the Soviet Union, a move that brought about an event now known as the Cuban Missile Crisis. In the summer of 1962, Soviet premier Nikita Khrushchev agreed to install defense weapons, including a number of nuclear missiles, on Cuban soil. The launchpads were kept under Soviet control, however, and more than 40,000 Soviet troops accompanied the weapons. When U.S. president John F. Kennedy learned from the CIA of the buildup, he publicly denounced it on October 22 of that year as a "clandestine, reckless, and provocative threat to world peace."

Kennedy immediately ordered U.S. aircraft carriers to quarantine the island to halt any more weapons shipments and demanded that those missiles already in place be withdrawn. For several days, it appeared that an all-out nuclear war might errupt. Finally, on October 28, Khrushchev agreed to U.S. demands on the condition that the United States would never invade Cuba.

Castro was enraged by the Soviets' backing down over the missiles, but there was little he could do. His government had made repeated attempts in the early 1960s to turn Cuba into a self-sufficient, industrialized nation, but those efforts failed disasterously through poor planning and a lack of resources and trained personnel. A large Soviet combat force remained behind after the other troops had been withdrawn. Still, Castro insisted on his nation's independence, proclaiming in March 1967: "This revolution will never be anybody's satellite or yes-man." The following year, however, he publicly endorsed the USSR's invasion of its European neighbor, Czechoslovakia.

After a failed 1970 sugarcane harvest, Castro sought other ways to improve on production and efficiency. In 1972, Cuba joined the Council for Mutual Economic Assistance, an organization established to coordinate the economies of Soviet-bloc countries; in 1974, Leonid Brezhnev became the first Soviet leader to make an official tour of Cuba; and, in 1976, the Cuban government at last adopted a new constitution—based on the Soviet model.

*In 1962, Soviet premier Nikita Khrushchev and Fidel Castro completed an agreement to install nuclear missiles in Cuba as a defense against a possible U.S. invasion. President John F. Kennedy ordered a U.S. quarantine of the island to halt further arms shipments and demanded the removal of those missiles already installed.*

During the 1970s Cuba and the USSR began to work together to support Marxist governments and revolutionary forces worldwide. In 1975, Cuba began to send large numbers of its own troops—armed with Soviet weapons and equipment—to fight with Marxist forces in Angola, Ethiopia, and Mozambique. In the late 1970s the Cuban army was the second most powerful in the Western Hemisphere, and Cuban military advisers were serving in more than 20 countries.

In 1980 Cuba suffered a dramatic wave of emigration when Castro attempted to defuse an embarrassing situation. Thousands of Cubans had sought asylum with the United States through the Peruvian embassy that March, and Castro responded by opening the port of Mariel to anyone who wished to leave Cuba. Over 125,000 discontented Cubans fled on boats to Florida before the open-immigration policy ended in October. Among the Mariel boat people were several thousand criminals and mental patients whom Castro had allegedly wished to "dump" in the United States. In all, between 1959 and the end of 1980, more than a million Cubans had chosen to leave the country, even when it was illegal to do so without special permission.

In 1983 Cuban forces clashed with U.S. Marines and local forces on the tiny Caribbean island of Grenada, following a Marxist takeover there. The Cuban troops were forced to withdraw, in their first major military defeat. In 1992, following other withdrawals, Castro announced that Cuba would no longer support insurgent movements in other countries.

By the 1980s, Cuba's economic dependence on the Soviet Union had grown to the level of $5 billion in subsidies a year. The *perestroika* (restructuring) policies of the Soviet Union's Mikhail Gorbachev destabilized this arrangement in the late 1980s. Then the dissolution of the USSR in 1991, which effectively ended the flow of aid, triggered the worst economic crisis in Cuba's history. Between 1990 and 1994, the economy contracted by 40 percent. Foreign trade fell by one-third, and by 1995 the country was using only half the amount of energy that it had before 1991.

The Cuban populace, already at a low standard of living, now suffered widespread shortages of food and medicine, soap, and other basic goods. In 1990 Castro declared a Special Period in Peacetime (Período Especial) to try to deal with the economic emergency through stricter rationing and other policies, and in 1992 the Cuban constitution was revised.

By 1994, thousands of Cubans were setting to sea in small, improvised rafts for the United States, a dangerous journey of some 90 miles which only half were estimated to survive. In August, rioting broke out in Havana when police intercepted an outbound vessel. When Castro (echoing his actions in 1980) announced he would not prevent people from leaving, a wave of small craft departed. In one month, U.S. Coast Guard ships picked up nearly 35,000 *balseros* (rafters), interning them at Guantánamo Bay. Eventually all were admitted to the United States.

In February 1996, Cuban pilots shot down two aircraft over the Caribbean—inside what Cuba claimed were its territorial waters—killing four Cuban-Americans, members of Brothers to the Rescue, a group dedicated to picking up Cuban rafters and leafleting mainland Cuba. In response, the U.S. Congress passed the Helms-Burton Act, making it possible for individuals to sue foreign companies in U.S. courts for damages from their use of properties seized during the Revolution, and denying U.S. visas to foreign investors in Cuba. This policy further complicated prospects for Cuba and the United States to settle Cuba's outstanding debts and normalize economic relations.

Meanwhile, the early 1990s had seen Cuba taking cautious steps toward a market economy and actively pursuing new trading partners to replace the Soviet Union. With direct foreign investment now allowed, Canada undertook some ambitious projects, particularly in mining and tourism. Spain and Mexico also invested, and Cuba embarked on trading agreements with China, Russia, and others. By the mid-1990s Cuba's GDP (gross domestic product) had finally begun to grow again.

*Young Cubans salute their national flag as they prepare for the new school year.*

# 6

# The Cuban Way of Life

In 1996, Cuba's population was estimated to be 11.1 million people, and about 74 percent of that number lived in urban areas. In spite of government efforts to discourage urbanization, Cuba's urban population has continued to grow.

Many, though not all, of Cuba's larger cities lie along the coast, on or near the deep bays that form natural harbors. The largest of these cities is the nation's capital, Havana, home to more than 2 million people. Old Havana is the most popular area of the city because of its colonial fortresses, churches, and villas. New Havana, the section of the city that contains the government buildings, has many hotels and high-rise apartment buildings. Santiago — Cuba's second largest city, with about 444,000 residents—lies at the foot of the Sierra Maestra and next to a large, deep bay. Ranking third is the inland city of Camagüey, with about 294,000 people. Camagüey has thrived on cattle ranching and the sugar industry. Several smaller cities have populations of more than 100,000 people: Holguín, an industrial city where Cuba's large sugarcane harvesters are manufactured; Santa Clara, another manufacturing center that produces housewares; Guantánamo,

*Havana, the nation's capital, is the largest city in Cuba and is divided into two areas: New Havana and Old Havana. High rises and office buildings, hotels, and the commercial district are located in New Havana, which overlooks the harbor.*

which produces most of Cuba's salt; Cienfuegos, a harbor town and trading center for tobacco, fruits, and sugar; Pinar del Río, which is located in the middle of the best tobacco land in Cuba; and Matanzas, the sugar capital of the country.

## Ethnic Groups

The island's culture is a mixture of Spanish and African elements, and its population can be broken down into these ethnic groups. The Spanish and mulatto (people of mixed Spanish and African ancestry) groups together make up about 88 percent of the population, with those of pure African ancestry accounting for some 11 percent. One percent or less consists of Chinese, whose ancestors first came to Cuba as contract laborers in the mid-1800s. Whatever their ethnic background, all Cubans speak Spanish, which is also the nation's official language.

## Religion

Before Castro's rise to power, the overwhelming majority of Cubans identified themselves as Roman Catholics. This heritage reflects Spain's policy of promoting a unified culture as it began to colonize the Americas more than 400 years ago. Yet the alliance of the

Catholic church with the colonial government caused some lingering resentment, and Castro's government came into conflict almost immediately with religious leaders. Soon after coming to power, Castro expelled hundreds of priests, nuns, and layworkers from the country. In late 1961, the government banned all religious processions, abolished religious holidays, and slashed religious access to the media. Religious dissenters were among the many "improper" groups sentenced to labor camps during that decade.

However, the revised constitution of 1992 offered several gestures toward greater religious tolerance: the state was declared to be secular, rather than atheist; religious believers were allowed to belong to the Cuban Communist party, and discrimination for religious beliefs was outlawed.

A small percentage of the Cuban people practice a secretive religion known as Santería (also sometimes called *lucumí*). Santería was first practiced by the Yorubans of Africa. After many tribe members came to Cuba as slaves, their ancient beliefs slowly mingled with the Catholicism of the Spanish, producing a new, hybrid religion.

*The city of Trinidad, one of Cuba's most perfectly preserved colonial towns, overlooks the Caribbean coast and is situated in the foothills of the Sierra del Escambray. The city's cobblestoned streets, red tile roofs, and arched windows hark back to the days of Spanish rule.*

Santería derives its name from the Spanish word *santo*, or saint, and translates literally as "worship of the saints." Believers, called *santeros*, worship numerous Yoruban gods, known as *orishas*. Each orisha is identified with a particular Catholic saint; Saint Barbara, for example, is seen as the incarnation of Chango, the Yoruban god of fire, lightning, and thunder. Santeros also practice casting magic spells through the ritual use of herbs, oils, amulets, necklaces, and other objects.

## Holidays

The blending of Spanish and African cultures found in Santería is also seen in Cuba's annual Carnival, celebrated throughout the island in late July. The Carnival, comparable to the Mardi Gras in New Orleans, began with the celebration of Catholic holidays such as Epiphany (the manifestation of Christ to the Magi) and Shrove Tuesday (the day before the beginning of Lent, a period of penitence and fasting). As part of each town's *parrandas* (festivities), various religious societies formed by Cuba's slaves would parade through the streets, dancing, making music, and wearing masks; their drums

*The Carnival in Santiago de Cuba is celebrated in July. At Carnival, people eat, dance, and play music in the streets; as a folk festival, it is celebrated annually by several cities, each bringing its own traditions to the merry-making.*

and costumes celebrated their African folklore as much as the Cuban holiday.

Since the 1959 revolution, the various parrandas have been merged with a carnival traditionally observed in Santiago in late July, at the end of the sugarcane harvest. Because Castro tried to capture the Moncada army base at the height of the Santiago festivities—on July 26, 1953—Cuba's Carnival is now the national holiday and is officially celebrated as the Anniversary of the 1953 Revolt.

January 1 is no longer celebrated as New Year's Day but as Liberation Day, in observance of President Batista's flight from office in 1959. The first day of May marks International Workers' Day, which is observed with parades and is sometimes called May Day. The government also recognizes the second Monday in October as War of Independence Day, after the Grito de Yara (Battle Cry of Yara) of October 10, 1868.

## Labor, Industry, and Economy

Until the early 1990s, because the government had nationalized almost all jobs, almost 100 percent of the work force was employed by the government. But in 1993, private ownership of small businesses was permitted in some 100 trades, and farmers were allowed to sell their harvests directly at farmers' markets. By 1996, 200,000 Cubans owned licensed small businesses, out of a total active labor force of over 4.5 million workers. In another momentous change, in 1995 the government abandoned guaranteed employment for all workers, bringing unemployment back to Cuba for the first time in decades.

Although workers in almost all job fields belong to unions, the unions cannot legally strike for higher wages or other benefits. With the exception of holidays, most adults are expected to work a five-and-a-half-day week.

*Sugarcane harvesters roll down the assembly line at a factory in Holguín province in 1981. Although Cuba imports most of the machinery it uses, it has been successful in manufacturing the harvesters to help bring in the island's most important crop.*

Around 20 percent of Cuba's labor force is employed in agriculture, forestry, or fishing. The sugarcane harvest still requires many seasonal workers, but machines have reduced manual labor to some degree. Approximately 30 percent work in "service" occupations — a broad category covering white-collar jobs such as teaching, medicine, law, and government administration. Industry and commerce account for another 33 percent of the labor force. Cuba's main mineral resource is nickel, and many people work at either mining it or refining the raw ore into a purer form. Smaller deposits of chromium, cobalt, and copper are also processed and sold overseas.

Cuban industry is hampered by a lack of oil, natural gas, and coal deposits on the island from which to make fuel. A sugar-for-petroleum barter with Russia now supplies much of Cuba's oil. Much of the existing industry involves food preparation: sugar refining, meat packing, canning, milk processing, and similar activities. Other plants produce textiles, chemicals, fertilizer, and construction materials. Consumer goods, however, are in short supply. Like many basic food items, most consumer goods are available only through a complex rationing system.

Almost all Cubans are issued books of ration cards, and people often wait in long lines for whatever goods are obtainable. This system covers everything imaginable, from bath soap to coffee and from tennis shoes to cosmetics. Even sugar, the island's largest crop, is rationed because most of it is exported. Many items are simply unavailable.

Because of rationing, fish has become a common staple of the Cuban diet; pork, beef, and chicken are widely preferred but are scarce. Generally, Cuban cooking is a mixture of traditional Spanish foods with Caribbean fruits and vegetables. One very popular dish is rice with black beans called *moros y cristianos*. Others include *arroz con pollo* (chicken and rice), *ropa vieja* (shredded flank steak), and *cerdo asado* (roast pork). Side dishes of fried plantains, sweet potatoes, cassava, and malanga (a root resembling a sweet potato) are also common. Because most fruits are exported, they are often hard to find, but popular desserts include guava pastries and custard topped with burned sugar (flan).

Just as France is famous for its wines, Cuba is famous for its rum, a liquor distilled from sugarcane. Rum is the basis for such famous cocktails as the *mojito* and the daiquiri. Cubans are also notoriously fond of strong coffee and a sweet drink called *guarapo*, which is pure sugarcane juice on ice.

## Recreation and Sports

Because most Cubans cannot travel outside their country, many spend their vacations on the island's beautiful beaches, where they can snorkel, water-ski, surf, and scuba dive. Cuba also has several national forests and, near Havana, the large Lenin Park, named after the Soviet leader Vladimir Lenin, which offers palm trees, fishing lakes, picnic areas, an aquarium, an art gallery, and the nearby National Botanical Garden.

A deep-sea fishing contest is held annually at Marina Hemingway, west of Havana, awarding a cup donated by the American novelist Ernest Hemingway. Hemingway himself enjoyed such Cuban sports as cockfighting and jai alai (a ball game similar to racquetball).

Cubans are passionate about baseball. The Cuban national baseball team has achieved preeminence in international competition, with over 20 world championships, including the gold medal at the 1992 and 1996 Olympics.

The government's heavy support of athletic training, starting with special secondary schools for athletes (EIDEs), has reaped an extraordinary record for this small country in international athletic competition. Its outstanding athletes include Alberto Juantorena, winning runner at the 1976 Olympics, world-record-holding high jumper Javier Sotomayor, and heavyweight boxer Teofilo Stevenson, who won gold medals in the 1972, 1976, and 1980 Olympics. Track star Ana Fidelia Quirot returned from serious burn injuries to win a silver medal in the 1996 Olympics.

*Members of the Cuban baseball team carry their flag around the field at the Centennial Summer Olympics in Atlanta. Cuba won the gold medal.*

## Men and Women

*Machismo*—the public display of intense, aggressive masculinity—is a tradition shared by many Latin American cultures, dating back to the first Spanish conquistadores. At its finest, the macho ideal stands for strength, bravery, and daring; at its worst, it signifies brutality, boasting, and recklessness. Many historians argue that this tradition helps to explain South America's penchant for the caudillo—the military dictator who rules through a mixture of charisma and force.

To help change the macho attitudes of the island, the Federation of Cuban Women was established in 1960 to incorporate women into every segment of Cuban society. It has sponsored such programs as the Ana Betancourt Schools for Peasant Girls (Ana Betancourt fought for Cuba's independence during the 1860s and for the liberation of women) and day-care centers, and it helped win passage of the Family Code in 1975, which, among other things, requires that both partners in a marriage must help in running the home.

Although traditional relations between men and women have shown great persistence, one indication of progress for women was the outcome of the first direct elections to the National Assembly in 1993. Of all delegates elected, 22.7 percent were women, a percentage exceeded only by the governmental bodies of Scandinavia.

*Raúl and Fidel Castro attend a meeting in Havana in 1977. Fidel, who has been head of state since 1959, is the first secretary of the Cuban Communist party and the president of the Council of State.*

# 7

# The Party and Government

The Cuban government today operates on the basis of a constitution enacted in February 1976 and modeled after the Soviet Union's 1936 constitution. This document provides for the fundamental principles of Cuban society and the rights and responsibilities of the people and government. One of the most important features of the constitution is the power it gives to the Communist party. Virtually all the leaders of Cuba's government belong to the party's influential Central Committee, the decision-making body that establishes economic and political guidelines.

The constitution was revised in 1992, eliminating references to the former Soviet bloc and authorizing secret-ballot elections to the National Assembly from pre-approved slates of candidates. The revisions softened the Communist economic structure by ending the state monopoly on trade, allowing private investment in some state companies and recognizing foreign ownership in joint economic ventures. The amendments also endorsed greater religious tolerance.

The modern Cuban Communist party (Partido Comunista de Cuba, or PCC) emerged in 1965 after Fidel Castro, the head of state since 1959, united the country's existing political groups. At that time Castro personally selected the members of the PCC's top three bodies: the Central Committee, the Political Bureau, and the

Secretariat. Since the party was first organized, Fidel and Raúl Castro have served, respectively, as its first secretary and second secretary.

The PCC is not a political party like the Democratic and Republican parties in the United States. Membership in the party is achieved through nomination, and the organization has traditionally allowed only some 5 percent or less of the population to join. It carefully screens all possible members for suitability. This screening process begins early in life with Los Pioneros (the Pioneers), a nationwide youth organization for children between the ages of 5 and 14. At age 14, some Pioneers move on to the more selective Communist Youth Union (Unión de Jovenes Comunistas, or UJC). Communist Youth members carry out labor and social projects, study Marxism, and engage in military training. They become eligible to join the PCC at age 27, ensuring a variety of personal and professional advantages.

The Communist party continues to be Cuba's only legal political organization. By the mid-1990s, some sixty dissident political groups existed, but they faced chronic harassment by the government.

Under the 1976 constitution, Cuba is divided into 14 provinces, which are in turn composed of 169 municipalities. Cuban citizens may vote for their municipal delegates, who are not required to be Communist party members. However, campaigning is prohibited, so elections cannot become forums to express opinions on government policies.

The 169 municipalities elect delegates to higher assemblies. All of these assemblies, however, meet only occasionally. When they are not in session, their power is exercised by executive committees, and membership in these committees is controlled by local boards dominated by the Communist party (PCC).

The National Assembly of People's Power (Asamblea Nacional del Poder Popular) originally drew its members from the municipal assemblies and from PCC nominations. In 1993, the first direct elections for this body, from slates approved by special candidate commissions, led to an assembly of 589 members. These members serve five-year terms but on a part-time basis. When it is not in session, the National Assembly's powers are exercised by a full-time Council of State, whose members the National Assembly elects.

The Council of State consists of 31 members, headed by a president and first vice-president. Since the constitution first went into effect, Fidel and Raúl Castro have served as president and first vice-president, respectively. The Council of State holds most governmental decision-making authority.

As president, Fidel Castro also selects the heads of all government ministries. These ministries form a vast bureaucracy covering all aspects of Cuban life, and their top officials collectively form a third political body called the Council of Ministers. This council also possesses wide-ranging powers, such as conducting foreign policy and trade, drafting the national budget, and overseeing national security. Since the constitution first went into effect, Fidel and Raúl Castro, as president and first vice-president, have led the Council of Ministers. Raúl has also served as minister of the armed forces and Fidel as commander in chief.

Finally, a national judiciary, or court, also operates under the constitution, headed by the People's Supreme Court. This body is not, however, comparable to the U.S. Supreme Court. Its members are appointed by and responsible to the National Assembly, and it has no power to rule on constitutional issues, a power that is left to the assembly (or, more often, to the Council of State). Instead, the People's Supreme Court is administrative and breaks down into five smaller bodies, each concerned with a different legal field: the Criminal Court, the Civil and Administrative Court, the Labor Court, the Military Court, and the Court for State Security. Beneath these high courts exists a system of provincial and municipal courts.

The official attitude toward civil liberties—such as freedoms of speech, religion, and the press—is that these are privileges willingly sacrificed by the Cuban people to assure the revolution's aims. Article 61 of the constitution specifies that "none of the freedoms which are recognized for the citizens may be exercised contrary to . . . the existence and objectives of the socialist state." Questioning the state is thus labeled an unproductive, even harmful activity that most citizens shun in exchange for social progress. As evidence of this progress, Cuban officials generally point to Cuba's high literacy rate and its extensive public health care system.

Most experts agree that health care and literacy have improved since Castro took over in 1959, especially in the Cuban countryside, where some 30 percent of the people still live. Although medical care was readily available in Cuban cities during the 1950s, it was quite rare in rural areas. The Castro regime stressed public health programs during its early years, and today numerous hospitals and outpatient clinics operate across the island. Doctors are employees of the state, and most medical care is free. Government statistics suggest that the nation's infant mortality rate (the number of babies who die at birth) is among the lowest in the world. In 1996, there were 8 infant deaths reported for every 1,000 live births.

Literacy in pre-Castro Cuba was actually among the highest in Latin America: Around 75 percent of the Cuban people in the mid-1950s could read and write. During Castro's rule, this percentage has officially increased to 96 percent, with the greatest improvement again made among the rural population.

The average yearly income of a Cuban worker is in line with the wages earned in neighboring countries. In the mid-1990s, Cuba's gross domestic product (GDP) amounted to $1,260 per capita in U.S. dollars. Cuba's basic unit of currency is the peso. Although it is officially equivalent to the U.S. dollar, its unofficial (black-market) value had dropped as low as 120 pesos to the dollar by 1994. In 1995 the government began legally trading the two currencies at their unofficial exchange rate, then 30 pesos to the dollar. Because of the international weakness of the Cuban peso, much of the nation's foreign trade has been on a barter basis. As it had with the Soviet Union, Cuban negotiated a major sugar-for-oil barter deal with Russia. Even so, Cuba's debt to Russia is estimated as high as $20 billion, with roughly $7 billion more owed to various Western banks and lenders.

Since the 1959 revolution, many new communities have been constructed in rural areas. These communities, such as La YaYa in the province of Villa Clara, are totally self-contained, with apartments, pharmacies, schools, and day-care centers. Cuba has had a severe housing shortage in the past, and one of the primary goals of the Castro government has been to provide adequate housing for the population.

Some of the other important areas requiring heavy spending by the state include the media, the transportation system, and the education system. In free-market economies, the media—TV, radio, magazines, and newspapers—are generally privately owned and operate with income from commercial advertising. In Cuba, however, under Article 52 of the constitution, "organs of the mass media are state or social property." All are therefore funded by the government, which runs them and has ultimate control over their content.

Cuba's foremost newspaper is *Granma*, published daily in Havana. Granma serves as the official voice of the Communist party and has a circulation of about 750,000 copies. There are numerous smaller newspapers and a wide variety of magazines, such as *Muchacha* (Girl), for young women; *Verde Olivo* (Olive Green), for the armed forces; and *Tropicana*, a magazine of music and popular culture. The state also runs two news bureaus: Agencia de Información Nacional (National Information Agency, or AIN) and Prensa Latina (Latin Press).

More than 100 radio stations broadcast the news and music of several networks; the most important radio networks include Radio Rebelde (Rebel Radio) and Radio Progreso (Progress Radio). A shortwave network, Radio Habana Cuba, broadcasts internationally in several languages, including two South American Indian languages. The nation's two television networks, Canal Tele Rebelde (Rebel TV) and Canal 6 (Channel 6), broadcast mostly sports, military parades, government functions and speeches, educational programs, and state-approved news.

Like the media, most Cuban transportation is state owned and operated. The nation's major airline, Cubana, flies international routes to Canada, South America, Europe, and Russia. Cuba has the only functioning railway system in the Caribbean, with about 9,000 miles (14,640 kilometers) of track. Most of this is narrow-gauge railway reserved for the sugar industry, leaving 2,900 miles (4,700 kilometers) for passenger service.

In 1996, Cuba had an estimated 9,000 miles (14,575 kilometers) of paved roads, highlighted by Central Highway, which snakes over the length of the island from Santiago in the east to Pinar del Río in the west. Most secondary and farm-to-market roads are made of gravel or dirt, and many become unpassable during the annual rainy season.

A nationwide bus service provides the principal means of public travel—very few Cubans own cars. By 1996, there were an estimated 240,000 automobiles on the island, or around 2 for every 100 people. Foreign visitors commonly report their astonishment at the well-preserved U.S. Studebakers, Packards, and Plymouths (all dating from the 1950s) still cruising Cuban city streets. These cars' only competition are a few Ladas—Soviet-made autos reserved for government and Communist party officials, doctors, and sports stars. Rural farmers and ranchers commonly travel on horseback even today, and bicycles are common.

Much of the government's capital goes into its massive education system, which is free from elementary school through the university level. The state operates day-care and preschool centers for babies and children (starting at the age of 45 days) as a way of encouraging mothers to work outside the home. Children begin school at age six and must attend school through the sixth grade. At the secondary (high school) level, students might attend a technical (vocational) school; an elementary teacher–training school; or a basic school, which can lead to college or other higher training. Hundreds of thousands of rural students live at boarding schools and visit their homes only on weekends.

All Cuban students, from the time they attend elementary school to the completion of college, must work without pay for half of each school day. In rural boarding schools, for example, half the school body works in fields—planting, weeding, or harvesting—in the mornings, and the other half attends classes; the two groups then trade places in the afternoons. In the cities, students work on assembly lines or at other simple industrial tasks.

In the mid 1990s, about 200,000 students were active in higher education. The government stresses practical studies that will materially benefit the nation, such as teacher training, technology, the sciences, and agriculture. All students study Marxist philosophy and economics. Most graduates can expect to spend two to three years on special government assignments. These sometimes take the form of foreign service in a poorer country.

The Cuban armed forces were heavily supported by Soviet money, training, and equipment through the 1980s. As of the early 1990s, Cuba was believed to possess a military arsenal that included more than 1,000 tanks, more than 300 jet fighters, hundreds of short-range missiles, and several torpedo-bearing submarines. All men must serve 3 years in a branch of the military; the army, navy, and air force together are believed to total nearly 200,000 troops. The island's civilians, including women, are also heavily mobilized in various semi-military forces, such as the Militia of Territorial Troops, which involves more than 1 million people.

*Alicia Alonso, prima ballerina and founder of the National Ballet of Cuba, dances in her native country.*

# 8

# The Arts

Cuba has a diverse and rich heritage in the arts—music, dance, film, painting, and literature. Cuban art owes its distinctive identity to the blending of the Spanish and African art traditions.

## Music

People throughout the world recognize and enjoy the unmistakable sound of Afro-Cuban popular music and jazz, much of which celebrates the blending of the Spanish guitar and the African drum. During the early 20th century, Havana became a center of musical activity. The city's nightclubs, dance halls, and carnivals drew talented musicians much as they did in the birthplace of American jazz, New Orleans. Since then, songs and instrumental dances such as the mambo, the conga, the cha-cha, and the rumba have poured from generations of Cuban musicians, singers, and bands. A few of the most popular names in music include Chano Pozo; Frank "Machito" Grillo; Mario Bauza; Xavier Cugat; Arturo "Chico" O'Farrill; Celia Cruz, called the Queen of *Salsa*; and Gloria Estefan and her band, the Miami Sound Machine.

Cuba's first great composer was Ignacio Cervantes (1847–1905), a Havana-born concert pianist. His graceful and romantic *Danzas Cubanas* (Cuban Dances) are still played by pianists today.

Cervantes' best-known successor, Alejandro García Caturla (1906–40), wrote many folk-influenced works such as the choral piece "Yamba-O," a musical arrangement of a poem by Cuban writer Alejo Carpentier. Today Cuba's foremost composers are Leo Brouwer (born in 1939) and Aurelio de la Vega (born in 1925).

Ernesto Lecuona (1896–1963) wrote both serious works and hit popular songs, such as "Siboney" and "Malagueña." He played in recital halls and in Hollywood, working on musical films such as *Under Cuban Skies* and *Carnival in Costa Rica*. Popular songwriter-singers of more recent times include Beny Moré, Silvio Rodríguez (who created the *nueva trova*, a type of poetic-political song), and Joseito Fernández. The contemporary band Los Irakere performs jazz-rock, whereas singer Celina Gonzalez has recorded albums of *musica campesina*, or Cuban country music.

The exciting rhythms of Afro-Cuban music have inspired composers and musicians around the world. As long ago as 1875, France's Georges Bizet wrote a Cuban-influenced "Habanera" for his opera *Carmen*. In the 20th century, the American composer George Gershwin was moved to write his *Cuban Overture* after several visits to the island. Gershwin's colorful 1932 overture uses several percussion instruments native to Cuba: the bongo drums; claves, or rhythm sticks; maracas, a kind of rattle; and the *guiro*, a notched gourd that is scraped to produce a rasping sound. The rhythms of mambo influenced such American jazz musicians as Stan Kenton, Artie Shaw, and Dizzy Gillespie.

Two current exemplars of rumba are Los Muñequitos de Matanzas and Grupo AfroCuba. Adalberto Alvarez and his group Son 14 have updated the more melodic *son* tradition of the Oriente region. And the popular group Síntesis strives to integrate jazz, rock, Afro-Cuban, and African sounds.

Today the island's most accomplished classical musician, pianist Frank Fernández, makes his home in Havana. The capital also supports a symphony orchestra, the Orquesta Sinfónica Nacional.

## Dance

The highly esteemed National Ballet of Cuba, located in Havana, made its debut in 1948 and has gained international acclaim under the direction of its founder, Alicia Alonso. Alonso, a Cuban-born ballerina who made her own youthful reputation with New York's American Ballet Theater, toured her company internationally until the Batista regime withdrew its funding in 1956. Her company disbanded, and Alonso danced in exile until the revolution in 1959, when she returned to Cuba to reestablish the National Ballet. The nation's newest ballet star is Carlos Acosta, who at age 16 won the gold medal in Switzerland's 1990 Prix de Lausanne competition.

Unfortunately, although the abstract arts of music and dance have endured, adapting to life in modern Cuba, the Castro regime has exercised rigid control over the arts of film, painting, and literature. With complete domination over film production, art exhibitions, and book publishing, the state not only determines what is *not* seen but has actively directed artists in producing "politically positive" work. This process began early in Castro's rule, when the government suppressed an art film, *PM*, for being "decadent." Soon after, in June 1961, Castro laid down his official arts policy: "What are the rights of writers and artists? . . . Within the [limits of] the revolution, everything; outside the revolution, nothing."

## Film

Because creating movies is an expensive enterprise, pre-Castro Cuba relied a great deal on the United States for its film entertainment. All kinds of Hollywood views of the island can be seen in *Weekend in Havana*, a colorful World War II musical, and the 1949 *Holiday in Havana* starring bandleader-actor Desi Arnaz. The 1956 adventure *Santiago* featured Alan Ladd as a gunrunner during the 1895 War of Independence and even included an appearance by an actor portraying revolutionary hero José Martí.

A few native Cuban filmmakers were, however, active in the 1950s, and upon taking power, Castro steered their production facilities toward making newsreels under the newly created Cuban Film Institute, or the ICAIC (Instituto Cubano del Arte e Industria Cinematográfica). The 1960 *Newsreel No. 49*, for example, denounced Hollywood movies for "producing an apology for imperialism and preaching violence and crime." Since then, the ICAIC has concentrated heavily on similar newsreels and documentaries, producing only a few feature films each year. Cuba's best-known documentary filmmaker, Santiago Álvarez, provided a moving biography of North Vietnam's president Ho Chi Minh in his 1969 movie *79 Springtimes*. Manuel Octavio Gómez's *The First Charge of the Machete*, made in 1969, is one of Cuba's most artistic and experimental films, dealing with the 1870 uprising against Spanish occupation.

Cuba's most acclaimed film director was Tomás Gutiérrez Alea (1928–96). His 1994 *Fresa y chocolate* (Strawberry and Chocolate) was nominated for an Academy Award for Best Foreign Film. His 1968 *Memorias del subdesarrollo* (Memories of Underdevelopment, or Inconsolable Memories), based on a novel by Cuban author Edmundo Desnoes, won several international prizes. Gutiérrez Alea's other films include the 1988 *Cartas del parque* (Letters from the Park).

Most moviegoers have probably seen one of the films shot by Cuban exile Nestor Almendros. He began his career directing short Cuban films such as *Gente en la playa* (People on the Beach) but went on to earn a worldwide reputation as a cinematographer, or film photographer. Almendros has made dozens of films in both Europe and America, working with such famous directors as François Truffaut and Martin Scorsese. He has also taken time from his cinematography career to direct two documentaries about political prisoners in Castro's Cuba: *Improper Conduct* (1984) and *Nobody Listened* (1988).

The first film school in Latin America was established in Havana in 1987. Under the supervision of Argentine director Fernando Birri, students are able to study the history and technology of filmmaking.

## Visual Art

Cuba possesses an old and honored tradition in painting. In the late 1700s, the Cuban-born black artist Vicente Escobar (1757–1834) was noted for his portraits of the island's wealthy peninsulares and criollos. During the 19th century, Esteban Chartrand (1840–83) painted romantic visions of tropical Cuban landscapes.

A trio of artists stand out in the early 20th century: Amelia Pelaez (1896–1968), Carlos Enríquez (1900–57), and Wilfredo Lam (1902–83). All three, although dealing with native subjects, were influenced by the powerful currents of European art; Lam's painting *Jungle* has been especially admired for its surrealistic use of Afro-Cuban symbols. Two other noted artists of the early 1900s are Marcel Pogolottis and René Portocarrero.

*A woman carefully paints a ceramic pitcher in a pottery plant on the Isle of Youth. In addition to ceramics, Cuba is noted for the marble that is quarried on the Isle of Youth and used by native sculptors.*

*The Presidential Palace in Havana now houses the Museum of the Revolution, commemorating Castro's victory over Batista.*

Ana Mendieta (1948–85) was sent to the United States as a teenager, but she visited Cuba and created artwork there as an adult. Her sculptures and the performance-based works of her *Silueta* series often incorporated her own body, connecting it symbolically to the earth and by extension to her lost homeland. Elements of Santería also entered her work. Though she died in her thirties, Mendieta's work has influenced a number of Cuba's younger generation of artists.

Although overt criticism of the current regime is not possible, many contemporary artists use irony, humor, and imaginative materials to explore sensitive issues. Carlos Cardenas, now living in Miami, has used the imagery of *balsas*, the makeshift rafts of the Cuban emigrants, in his sculptural installations. The *balsas* have also inspired artists still living in Cuba, including Luis Gomez and Kcho (Alexis Leyra), who has constructed oars in the shapes of crutches, machetes, and palm trees.

The Museo Nacional in Havana is Cuba's national museum for the fine arts. In 1993, the Wilfredo Lam Center opened its galleries in a renovated mansion in Havana. Since 1984, Cuba has hosted the Havana Biennial, an ambitious bi-yearly international art exhibition featuring the work of Cubans, South Americans, and artists of other Third World countries. The government also supports a number of historical museums, including Havana's Museum of the Revolution.

## Literature

Cuba's native literature is intertwined with its bitter political history. The great revolutionary hero José Martí (1853–95) is remembered not only as a patriot but as a poet and author. Some of his best work was collected in the volumes *Ismaelillo* and *Versos sencillos* (Simple Verses).

Another notable literary figure of the 19th century was Gertrudis Avellaneda (1814–73). Her novel *Sab*, published in Spain in 1841, was one of the first antislavery novels ever written. The 1882 novel *Cecilia Valdés*, by Cirilio Villaverde (1812–94), is still considered one of the country's most enduring works because it touches on the topics of racial intermarriage, social class, and racial oppression.

During the first half of the 20th century, two Cubans established international literary reputations: the novelist Alejo Carpentier (1904–80) and the poet Nicolás Guillén (1902–89). Carpentier's major works include *El reino de este mundo* (The Kingdom of This World), published in 1949, and *Los pasos perdidos* (The Lost Steps), published in 1952. Guillén has also served as chief of the nation's creative union, the Union of Writers and Artists of Cuba (Unión de Escritores y Artistas de Cuba, or UNEAC). A lifelong Communist,

*The American writer Ernest Hemingway lived in this house, now called the Hemingway Museum, from 1939 to 1961. Located in the town of San Francisco de Paula, the museum displays the writer's furniture, books, and trophies. A nearby village was the setting for Hemingway's* Old Man and the Sea.

he received the USSR's Stalin Prize in 1953, and Castro personally honored him in 1961 as Cuba's "national poet."

Artistic migration between Cuba and America has worked both ways in the past, as is demonstrated by the island's most famous literary figure, Ernest Hemingway, who made Cuba his home from 1939 to 1961. Although born in the United States, Hemingway wrote his most popular story, *The Old Man and the Sea*, with a Cuban backdrop and a Cuban fisherman as its hero.

Fluent in Spanish, Hemingway spent much of his adult life outside Havana at his spacious estate, called Finca Vigía, or Lookout Farm. There he wrote such major works as *For Whom the Bell Tolls* and for relaxation sailed the Gulf Stream in his yacht, the *Pilar*. Hemingway, a constant traveler, was in many ways an international citizen, but he once told reporters that after his many years at Finca

Vigía he thought of himself as a true Cuban. After he received the 1954 Nobel Prize in literature, he presented the gold medal to the shrine of Cuba's national saint, the Virgen de la Caridad del Cobre (the Virgin of El Cobre), located northwest of Santiago. Today Finca Vigía is preserved as a popular museum, and Hemingway continues to be one of the most widely read authors in Cuba.

Today Cuba's best-known literary figures include the poet Heberto Padilla, now living in New York, and the novelist Guillermo Cabrera Infante, now living in London, England. Cabrera Infante's second novel, *View of Dawn in the Tropics*, is a lyrical view of Cuban history told as fiction; the island itself seems to be the hero of this short, beautiful book.

*Cuban president Fidel Castro greets Jamaican prime minister P. J. Patterson at the Jose Marti airport in Havana. The reason for the visit is to explore the possibility of opening trade frontiers between Jamaica and Cuba.*

# 9

# The Future of Cuba

By the late 1990s, Fidel Castro had led the Cuban government for four decades. Although Cuba remained a Communist state, it faced many of the same stresses that had brought down the Communist regimes of Russia and Eastern Europe. The failures of its centralized economy, worsened by the loss of Soviet aid, led the Cuban government to limited experiments with free-market practices, such as private ownership of many small businesses and the establishment of free trade zones for foreign business ventures. But the legalization of U.S. currency, bringing needed cash to many families through their American relatives, also reintroduced economic inequalities. Even with a slow upturn in the country's overall wealth, many basic shortages remained, and the country's infrastructure suffered.

After Cuba's long history of domination by foreign powers (Spain, then the United States, then Russia), Castro seemed determined to lead the country into a new period of greater independence, dealing as a full-fledged partner with a number of other countries. Domestically, he was said to be following the Chinese model of introducing capitalist-style reforms within a political dictatorship. Some speculated that he would end up preserving only the most basic goals of the revolution: Cuban sovereignty, universal education, and health care.

Still, human-rights groups and other critics pointed to Cuba's continuing lack of free press and other media, its lack of free democratic elections, the harassment of political parties other than the Communist party, and the government's detention of a number of political prisoners. These factors, in addition to the continuing U.S. embargo, stood in the way of the restoration of normal relations between Cuba and its large neighbor to the north.

Many wondered about life after Castro, who turned a vigorous seventy in 1996. Though his brother Raúl remained his official successor, other, younger ministers could possibly take over. The anticipated transition, which could also lead Cuba to a new form of government, promised yet another test of the spirit of the Cuban people.

# GLOSSARY

**archipelago**
A chain of islands. Cuba is the largest island in an archipelago known as the West Indies or the Antilles.

*balsero*
A rafter; refers to the thousands of Cubans who left the island on flimsy rafts attempting to emigrate to the United States in the 1980s and 1990s.

*bohío*
A simple hut made of palm fronds and bamboo. First built by Cuban Indians, it is still a common dwelling in poorer rural areas of the island.

*caudillo*
A military strongman who assumes political power and controls the affairs of a region or country.

**criollo**
A person of pure Spanish descent born in Cuba.

**Grito de Yara**
The Battle Cry of Yara. On October 10, 1868, in the city of Yara, this declaration began Cuba's first war for independence. On February 24, 1895, the Grito de Baire opened the second, successful war against Spain.

**habanera**   A Cuban musical form, named for the capital city of Havana. It is also a Cuban dance in slow duple time.

**machete**   A large, broad knife used in cutting sugarcane. It was also used as a military weapon in the 19th century.

*machismo*   The public display of intense, aggressive masculinity. In Cuba, this tradition dates back to the first Spanish conquistadores.

**mulatto**   A person of mixed Spanish and African ancestry.

**nationalization**   The ownership and control of formerly private businesses and property by the government. Under Fidel Castro, all industries and most farms have been nationalized.

**Partido Comunista**   The elite Cuban Communist party, formed out of existing groups in 1965. Today it is the only legal political party in Cuba.

*peninsular*   During the Spanish colonial era, a Spanish-born member of Cuba's ruling class.

**Platt Amendment**   U.S. provisions that were attached to the Cuban constitution giving the United States veto power over Cuba's diplomatic and fiscal relations with foreign powers, the right to intervene to preserve Cuban independence, and the right to lease a naval base in Cuba. Unworkable and very unpopular, the amendment was terminated in 1934.

**Santería**   Literally, "worship of the saints." A secretive religion combining the beliefs of Africa's Yoruban tribes with Spanish Catholicism. It first arose among Cuban slaves and is still practiced today.

**yellow fever**   A deadly tropical virus, so named because the victim's skin turns yellow from jaundice. A treatment for the disease, which is transmitted by  mosquitoes, was discovered in the early 1900s by Cuban and American doctors.

*zafra*   The annual sugarcane harvest.  The end of harvesting is celebrated with a nationwide three-day carnival in late July.

# INDEX

## A

Africa, 15, 31, 73, 78
Agrarian Reform Law, 69
Agriculture, 24, 25–26, 82
Alonso, Alicia, 97
Animal life, 26–27
Avallaneda, Gertrudis, 101

## B

Batista, Fulgencio, 62–64, 65–67, 69, 70
Bay of Pigs (Playa Girón), 71
Brezhnev, Leonid, 72
Brothers to the Rescue, 75
Brouwer, Leo, 96

## C

Cabrera Infante, Guillermo, 103
Camagüey (city), 32, 77
Camagüey (province), 21
Carib Indians, 31
Carnival, 80–81
Carpentier, Alejo, 101
Castro, Fidel, 15–17, 65–67, 69–75, 79, 87–89, 105–6
Castro, Raúl, 65, 69–70, 88–89, 106
Cervantes, Ignacio, 95
Céspedes, Carlos Manuel de, 43
Chartrand, Esteban, 99
Chibás, Eduardo, 65
Ciego de Avila (province), 21
Cienfuegos (city), 42, 71, 78
Cienfuegos (province), 21
City of Havana (province), 21

Columbus, Christopher, 15, 19, 24, 29, 31, 35
*Conquistadores*, 31–33
Council for Mutual Economic Assistance, 72
*Criollos*, 33, 34
Cuba
  arts, 95–103
  climate, 22–24
  constitution, 72, 74, 87, 88
  diet, 83
  economy, 17, 74, 75, 81–83, 90, 105
  education, 16, 92–93
  ethnic groups, 78
  geography, 20–22
  health care, 16, 90
  holidays, 80–81
  housing, 91
  independence, 39–60
  Indian settlers, 29–31
  industry, 70, 81–82
  labor, 81–82
  military, 17, 62, 73–74, 93
  population, 77
  recreation, 83
  religion, 78–80
  Spanish colonization, 31–37
  sports, 84–85
Cuban Communist party (Partido Comunista de Cuba), 87–88
Cuban Missile Crisis, 71–72

## E

Emigration, 71, 73, 74

110

England, 34, 35, 36
Enríquez, Carlos, 99
Escobar, Vicente, 99
Estefan, Gloria, 95
Estrada Palma, Tomás, 46, 60

F
Fernández, Frank, 96
Finlay, Carlos Juan, 58
Fishing, 26–27
France, 34, 36, 37

G
García, Calixto, 43, 45
García Caturla, Alejandro, 96
Gómez, Máximo, 43, 46
Gorbachev, Mikhail, 74
Government
    pre-Castro, 58–67
    under Castro, 69, 87–89
Granma (province), 21
Grau, Ramón, 62, 64
Grenada, 20, 74
Guanahacabibe Indians, 29
Guantánamo Bay, 57, 59
Guantánamo (city), 77
Guantánamo (province), 21
Guevara, Ernesto "Che", 65
Guillén, Nicolás, 101–2
Gutiérrez Alea, Tomás, 98

H
Haiti, 20, 34, 37
Havana (city), 32, 36, 45, 48, 77, 91, 95
Havana (province), 21
Havana, University of, 33, 61, 62, 65
Helms-Burton Act, 75
Hemingway, Ernest, 84, 102–3
Holguín (city), 77

Holguín (province), 21

I
Isla de la Juventud (Isle of Youth), 21

J
Juantorena, Alberto, 84

K
Kennedy, John F., 72
Khrushchev, Nikita, 72

L
Lam, Wilfredo, 99
Las Tunas (province), 21
Lecuona, Ernesto, 96
Literacy, 90
Literature, 101–3
Los Pioneros, 88

M
Maceo, Antonio, 43, 45, 46, 47
Machado, Gerardo, 61–62
McKinley, William, 47–48, 59
Magoon, Charles, 60
Mariel, 73
Martí, José, 45–46, 101
Matanzas (city), 41–42, 78
Matanzas (province), 21
Media, 70–71, 91–92
Mendieta, Carlos, 62, 63
Moncada, 64
Monroe, James, 40–41
Monroe Doctrine, 40
Moré, Beny, 96
Music, 95–96

N
National Assembly of People's Power (Asamblea Nacional del Poder Popular), 85, 87, 88–89

*P*

Padilla, Herberto, 103
Painting, 99
Pelaez, Amelia, 99
*Peninsulares*, 33
People's Supreme Court, 89
Pico Real del Turquino, 22
Pinar del Río (province), 21
Pirates, 34–35
Plant life, 24–26
Platt Amendment, 59–60, 63
Popular Socialist party (PSP), 69
Pozo, Chano, 95
Prío, Carlos, 64
Puerto Príncipe, 32, 34

*R*

Río Cauto, 22
Rodríguez, Silvio, 96
Russia, 75, 91, 92, 105. *See also*
  Soviet Union

*S*

Sancti Spíritus (city), 32
Sancti Spíritus (province), 21
Santa Clara, 67, 77
Santería, 79–80, 100
Santiago de Cuba (city), 32, 42, 43,
  77, 81
Santiago de Cuba (province), 21
Seven Years' War, 36
Sierra del Escambray, 22
Sierra Maestra, 22, 77
Sierra de los Órganos, 22

Sierra del Rosario, 22
Slavery, 15, 31, 36, 40, 41, 42, 46
Sotomayor, Javier, 84
Soviet Union, 15, 16, 17, 70,
  71–75, 82, 87, 91, 105
Spain, 15, 17, 31–37, 39–45, 57, 75,
  78, 105
Stevenson, Teofilo, 84

*T*

Taíno Indians, 29–31
Teller Amendment, 57
Ten Years' War, 43–44
Tobacco, 24
Trade, 35–36, 74, 90–91
Transportation, 92

*U*

United States, 15, 17, 36, 40–67,
  71–75, 105, 106
USS *Maine*, 48, 59

*V*

Villa Clara (province), 21
Villaverde, Cirilio, 101
Viñales Valley, 22, 29

*W*

Welles, Sumner, 62
West Indies, 15, 19, 34
Weyler, Valeriano, 46–47, 48
Women, 85

*Z*

Zanjón, Pact of, 44, 45